M000024296
FOR: EVI & ILMAR
LOVE: V. LINDA & CO.
TERVISEKS!
2011

MARIKA BLOSSFELDT

Essential Nourishment

Recipes from My Estonian Farm

Your feel-good guide to
healthful eating and energized living,
one delicious meal at a time

•

Photographs by Jaan Heinmaa
Original artwork by Marika Blossfeldt
Design by Krista Saare and Marika Blossfeldt

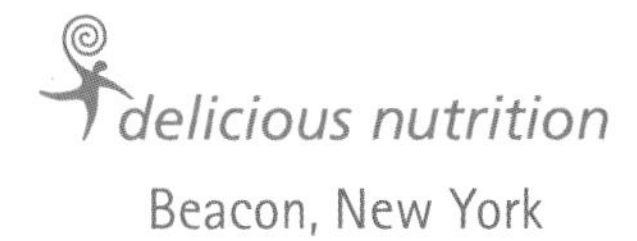

Beacon, New York

First English edition

Published in Estonian as *Looduslik toit. Täisväärtuslik elu*

Design	Krista Saare, Marika Blossfeldt
Photographs	Jaan Heinmaa, with portraits on page 289 and back flap by Hele-Mai Alamaa
Original artwork	Marika Blossfeldt
Production	Ave Karp

Photographed foods were prepared by Ursula Kukk, Marika Blossfeldt, Ave Karp, Janne Disko and participants in the 2008 cooking intensive at Polli Talu Arts Center.

The concepts of "Primary Foods" and "Secondary Foods" described on page 17 were developed at the Institute for Integrative Nutrition, which permitted the use of these terms. The figure on Yin and Yang Foods on page 29 was adapted from a similar figure in *The Self-Healing Cookbook* by Kristina Turner (Earthtones Press, 2002) and is used with permission. All trademarks are properties of their respective owners.

ISBN 978-0-615-42927-4

Library of Congress Control Number 2011920363

Published by Delicious Nutrition, Beacon, NY 12508

Printed by DiYA USA, Foster City, CA 94404

Distributed by Emerald Book Company

To order or request a bulk purchase discount, call the distributor at 512-891-6100 or send a written request to Emerald Book Company, PO Box 91869, Austin, TX 78709.

Order directly from the author at www.MarikaB.com/book.

Essential Nourishment offers general nutritional information intended for educational purposes only. It is not meant to be used for diagnosis or treatment of any health condition. Please consult your health-care professional if you have any concerns about your health.

I dedicate this book to all teachers who inspired, encouraged and enlightened me. **Frau Schüttler**, my elementary school teacher, who allowed me to draw on the blackboard during recess. **Dieter Klein**, my high school art teacher, whose passion for art and theater was infectious. **Ric Schachtebeck**, a performer and designer, who opened my mind and body to movement and dance. **Tamar Rogoff**, a New York-based choreographer, who taught me to move from the deep muscles close to the bones. **Ravi Hari Kaur**, my first yoga teacher, who introduced me to the dynamic and heart-centered practice of kundalini yoga. **Joshua Rosenthal**, director of the Institute for Integrative Nutrition, who taught me to think big.

Acknowledgments

I would like to thank and acknowledge Joshua Rosenthal and his staff for the profound learning and personal growth I experienced as a student and immersionist at the Institute for Integrative Nutrition in New York City. The Institute enabled me to create my own unique approach to nutrition, health and well-being. It taught me to merge ancient traditions with contemporary cutting-edge research and to foster deep respect for the innate internal wisdom of each human being. This book is very much rooted in the teachings of the institute as well as the teachings of my favorite lecturers and authors: Annemarie Colbin, Marc David, John Douillard, Sally Fallon, Steve Gagné and David Wolfe.

Many thanks to my editor, Paulette Schneider, who is as passionate about food as she is about words and who has made our collaboration a pure pleasure.

And my thanks to Daphne Hougham for proofreading.

My special thanks go to Hedina Christiner and Susan Osberg for commenting on my first draft.

Thank you, my yoga students, workshop and retreat participants and health coaching clients – you inspire me to keep on exploring and deepening my knowledge.

Thank you, Mando, for your love and support and for appreciating my cooking.

"Approach love and cooking with adventurous devotion."

His Holiness XIV Dalai Lama Tendzin Gjatso

Contents

Contents

Food Guides and Recipes

Figures

Tables

Introduction

How This Book Came About

I have always taken pleasure in eating good food. I feel very lucky that my mother was a diligent cook, and growing up in Germany I would enjoy three wholesome meals made from scratch every day. In this way our family got a lot of vitamins H and L – H is for homemade and L is for love. My father worked in the small town where I grew up, so most of the time we had all three meals together as a family. Mealtime was for sharing the day's events, and it was often a time of spirited conversation. I remember a lot of laughter as well.

I also enjoyed helping my mother prepare food for special occasions, such as holidays and meals when we expected guests. Having dinner with friends or relatives was very exciting to me. For one thing, it didn't happen too often – so when it did, the communal meal was always the highlight of the month. While the food was important, even more so was the social, emotional and spiritual connection shared by all who partook. We would sit for hours around the kitchen table and catch up with stories and life events. The kitchen was a favorite spot in our apartment – we hardly used the living room for our gatherings. Everybody naturally gravitated toward the kitchen. It was the true heart and soul of our home.

To this day, one of my favorite things to do is sit around a big table with a few friends, enjoy a delicious meal, drink some good wine, talk and laugh. I love cooking myself and entertaining guests, but I also enjoy sitting down to a set table when someone else has prepared the meal. It is such a treat!

Sharing a meal and communing with other souls is always an archetypal event for me. I believe the real reason why I created Polli Talu Arts Center (*Polli talu* means Polli's farm in Estonian) was simply to have ample opportunity to do just that. All summer long, numerous artists from all over the world and countless workshop participants from Estonia and elsewhere become extended family while residing at Polli Talu and enjoying lovely meals in great company.

I love the sensual aspect of food – how it looks, how it feels, how it smells and how it tastes. I even love the sound of cooking: the knock-knock of chopping vegetables, the chick-chick of cutting fresh herbs or the slow gurgling of boiling porridge. I hate to rush when I am cooking, as that cuts down my time to enjoy the whole process. I would rather put on some relaxing music and take my time. Cooking is very grounding for me. It is like a moving meditation, a practice of mindfulness. And if for some reason I do not have access to a kitchen for a while, I miss it dearly.

According to yogic numerology, the number eleven symbolizes the ability to integrate physical, subtle and spiritual energies. Eleven is the sum of the numbers of my birth date, and it might therefore not be a coincidence that another constant in my life has been the concept of integration. Coming from a visual arts background and moving into dance, I loved to integrate projected images with my dancing, creating multimedia performance works. Then, with heightened body awareness and a consciousness of energy flow through dance, I found it quite natural to take the next step of integrating yoga into my life. Adding nutrition – or as I prefer to say, nourishment – to energy work was an organic evolution as well. And so it made sense to study at the Institute for Integrative Nutrition in New York City and become a holistic health coach. Food is energy. Food is life force. Food is spirit.

The word "holistic" is derived from the Greek word *holos*, meaning all, entire, total. Holistic philosophy views the world as one universe in which everything is connected within a single all-encompassing conscious energy field. Each human spirit is part of the universal consciousness, with access to all existing information. At the same time, each human being is also a whole, mirroring the laws of the universe.

We experience our existence in this universe through mind, body, spirit and soul. The soul is our inner being, our true self. It is the quiet voice that gives us direction.

In order to really hear this quiet voice within, to truly understand ourselves and the reasons for our behavior and actions, we might need to calm our busy minds through meditation or other techniques that bring about inner awareness and mindfulness.

Our bodies, too, are born with innate intelligence, with a quiet voice on the cellular level – and I believe that everyone is capable of tapping into that well of knowledge within. If we pay attention to the messages our body sends, we can make personally appropriate choices – in food and in all other areas of life. Every human being is a unique creation, and there cannot be one way that fits all.

By heeding our inner voices, we can find our own way and create a life that brings joy and deep satisfaction. The answers to our questions are already within us – we need only to quiet down and listen.

Very much an "eleven," I enjoy integrating many parts to make a whole. Polli Talu Arts Center is a perfect example. It gives me the opportunity to integrate my background in the arts, my love of teaching, my understanding of architecture, my appreciation for beauty, my sense of detail, my ability to organize – and of course, my joy in serving delicious, wholesome meals to our guests.

Often our guests would praise the food and suggest that I write a cookbook. I put off the project for many years. But in the summer of 2007 during my weeklong wellness retreat at the center, the suggestion emerged again. My niece, Ave Karp, who happened to attend the retreat, looked at me and said, "Let's do it!" I looked at her and answered, "Let's do it!" And she took on the role of producer for this book project. So here it is: a long-overdue labor of love, an expression of appreciation for all that I have learned and a fulfillment of my desire to share.

How to Use This Book

If you use this book as just a cookbook, you will enjoy the simple, wholesome delicious meals you prepare. You will feel many positive effects from eating more whole and natural foods.

If you read through the nutrition chapters, you will better understand how nourishment is interconnected with your health and well-being. This understanding will bring more awareness and mindfulness to all aspects of your life.

But my hope is that you will treat this book as a step-by-step guide toward balance, vitality and joy. I suggest reading one chapter at a time. Once you have integrated the suggested healthy habits into your routines, move on to the following chapter. Each chapter is designed to build on the prior one, so it makes sense to start at the beginning and work sequentially.

To summarize most chapters or sections, I have recapped the essence of the material and suggested an action to help you incorporate its core teachings into your life.

May this book inspire you to spend more time in the kitchen preparing home-cooked meals, to be gentler to your body and more attentive to its needs, to feed your soul on a daily basis, to honor your body as a temple and reflection of your soul, and to begin a journey toward a new level of consciousness, kindness, communication and wellness.

May this book encourage you to take charge of your own health and well-being, to take responsibility for your life and to create the life you were meant to live. May it be fulfilling, inspiring, passionate – and delicious!

Food Is Not the Only Form of Nourishment

Do you remember a time when you just fell in love? Your senses were alive with excitement. Everything around you seemed to glow. Your feet barely touched the ground, you felt so uplifted and thrilled to be alive. You sat daydreaming by the window with a big smile on your face. Spending time with your lover sharing intimacy and laughter was enough to sustain you. You forgot about food completely because you were filled with happiness.

Or do you remember a time you worked on a fascinating project? You were completely engulfed in research or creative problem-solving. You felt deeply engaged, intellectually stimulated and empowered to be setting things in motion. Time and space no longer existed. The outside world became irrelevant. You were at your peak of productivity and confidence. The thought of food did not even cross your mind.

The way we live, as well as the foods we eat, affect our health and well-being. To codify this idea, Joshua Rosenthal, director of the Institute for Integrative Nutrition, coined the terms Primary Foods and Secondary Foods. He describes what we eat – our source of nutrients – as Secondary Foods, while Primary Foods are the other deeply nourishing elements in our lives that do not come on a plate.

Essence

The foods we eat sustain and regenerate our bodies. They create a solid base for our health and well-being. But exercise, work, relationships and spirituality nourish us on an even deeper level.

Action

Bring awareness both to your diet and to the other vital areas of your life. Notice how they nourish you in different ways. Ask yourself whether any area is out of balance and is calling for your attention.

Rosenthal's Primary Foods concept has four main components: physical activity, work and profession, relationships and spirituality.

The human body is designed to need regular physical activity in order to function at its best. A happy body is a moving body. Whether you enjoy working out at a gym, taking a dance class, going for walks or riding your bike – any moderate activity will keep your body fit and will benefit both physical and mental health.

As adults, many of us spend more hours of the day at work than at any other activity. It is crucial for our health that we enjoy the work we do, that we find it meaningful, engaging and fulfilling. It is also important that our work environment be appropriate for the task at hand and that the work atmosphere be pleasant. And it is essential that we get compensated fairly for our work.

Throughout our lives, we encounter many different relationships. We might consider our relationships with parents, children, teachers, friends, lovers, partners and colleagues to be most influential. They feed us on an emotional level. They provide a mirror that enables us to learn about ourselves and come to a better understanding of who we are. Harmonious and loving relationships create a safe, encouraging and nurturing environment that enables us to develop and thrive.

As work stimulates the intellect, exercise propels the mind and body and relationships strengthen the emotions, spirituality nourishes the soul. It doesn't matter what shape or practice spirituality takes in our lives, but it is important to acknowledge that we are spiritual beings and need to listen to our soul's yearnings. It is essential to our well-being that we engage in activities that feed our souls on a daily basis, whether those activities are prayer, meditation, spending time alone, listening to music or taking a walk in nature.

Even if we eat carrots all day long, we will not be completely healthy and happy if our fundamental needs are not fulfilled. On the other hand, a nourishing and grounding diet can provide just the right amount of support and stability we need to resolve imbalances in the fundamental areas of our lives.

Back to Basics: Water

All life on our planet Earth originated in the waters of the primordial oceans, and water continues to play an essential role in our lives today. We can go for a month without food, but we can live for only two or three days without water.

Water carries nutrients and oxygen to our cells and transports toxins out of the body. It plays many major roles in the creation of new life, from the fluids that lead to conception to the fluids that accompany birth. There is no metabolic function in the body that does not include water.

The body is made up of 65 percent water. This might seem hard to believe, but try to imagine your body on its cellular level. Each cell is made up of a thin wall surrounding a relatively small nucleus, and the rest is fluid – mainly water. Many internal and external conditions can lead to dehydration, so it makes sense that water needs to be replenished continually.

I recommend drinking spring water – bottled or from a trusted source – or filtered water. Tap water may contain chlorine, fluoride and sometimes even lead. If you have a water filter, make sure you use it according to the instructions provided and change the filter regularly.

How much water do you need to drink? It depends. If you are petite, you need less than someone who is tall. If you are physically very active, you need more than someone who is less active. If you consume dehydrating liquids like coffee, caffeine-containing teas and cola drinks or alcoholic beverages, you need more than someone who does not drink these liquids. If you live in a hot climate, you need more than someone who lives in a cool climate – however, do not underestimate the drying effects of winter, as both the cold wind outside and the central heating systems inside are extremely dehydrating.

Start to experiment and see how you feel. Definitely have some water first thing in the morning: one or two glasses. This will flush the kidneys, eliminating yesterday's toxins, and give your body a fresh start for the new day. "It's like taking an internal shower" is how my client Candida so eloquently put it.

When we reach adulthood, many of us lose our sense of thirst, which is so pronounced in children. By the time we feel thirsty, we are already seriously dehydrated. Think of having water as a preventative rather than as a remedy for dehydration.

Bring water with you at all times, whether you are moving about or working at your desk. If you keep a glass or bottle of water visible at your side, you will be more inclined to remember to take a sip once in a while. Have some water midmorning, about an hour before lunch. Avoid drinking large amounts with your meals because this dilutes the digestive juices. However, the digestive system benefits from being well moistened before the food starts arriving. So have some water about an hour to thirty minutes before eating. Sipping a little water with your meal is fine.

Be sure to have some water in the afternoon as well. We often experience a period of low energy in the afternoon, which many of us try to fix by reaching for sugary sweets or coffee. Often it is water that our bodies crave, but we misinterpret the message and think we need a boost of sugar or caffeine.

Drink as much water as you feel like having. Half a glass might be enough, but sometimes we don't realize how dehydrated we are and don't start feeling the thirst until we begin to drink some water. That first sip makes you realize: I am really thirsty! When that happens, drink until you feel satisfied. Always check in with your body – how do you feel, what do you need? If you have a sense that the water is just running through you (frequent urination and very pale urine), have smaller amounts of water more frequently.

Essence

Water is involved in all metabolic functions in the body. It is essential for survival and well-being.

Action

Start your day with one or two glasses of water. Drink water throughout the day. Experiment with the amount of water you need to find out what works for your body and your circumstances.

If you wake up in the middle of the night to use the bathroom, avoid drinking in the evening. If you wake up in the middle of the night with the sensation of a dry mouth, keep water by your bedside and have a sip when that happens.

Carry water with you when you are on the go. Hard plastic bottles are better than soft plastic bottles. There are also lightweight stainless steel water bottles available. You do not need to buy water if you have a water filter – just fill up your bottle at home and you are all set.

If you find plain water too boring, add some taste by making herbal teas (no caffeine!) or by adding a little lemon, lime or orange to your drinking water. A slice of cucumber, some rose petals or a fresh peppermint leaf can also dress up your water nicely and make it more interesting to drink. Coconut water is also excellent for hydration.

If cold water does not appeal to you, have warm or hot water. Drinking plain hot water can feel extremely soothing. In fact, there is an ayurvedic remedy for weight loss based on traditional Indian teachings: Boil water for fifteen minutes, pour it into a thermos and sip it throughout the day. The prolonged boiling makes the water molecules "sharper," enabling them to better penetrate any stagnation in the body and flush out toxins and fat.

So far, we have been talking about the effects of water on our bodies. Let's look now at how we affect water. Dr. Masaru Emoto has for many years been studying water and water crystals. He made a remarkable discovery: Water responds to words, whether they are spoken, written or even thought. Kind, uplifting words tend to produce beautifully shaped water crystals, while angry, discordant expressions have produced warped crystals.

Considering that almost three-quarters of the body consists of water, it makes sense that we need to be aware of our thoughts and spoken words. Words do have an effect on our own health and on the well-being of our loved ones, friends and colleagues. Dwelling on negative thoughts and events might bring us illness and disease, and focusing on positive thoughts can bring healing and happiness. How about greeting yourself in the mirror each morning with a cheerful thought and a big smile?

Whole Foods Create a Whole Body

"Whole foods" is a contemporary expression that was unnecessary in the days of our great-grandmothers. Back then, before the advent of industrial food processing, all food was naturally whole. Today we need to differentiate between whole and processed foods as a matter of survival.

Whole foods are grains, vegetables, roots, legumes, leafy greens, lettuces, mushrooms, herbs, fruits, berries, nuts, seeds, seaweeds, fish, meat, poultry, eggs and milk.

They are in their most natural state, complete as is, just the way Mother Nature provides them. They have not been artificially processed, stripped of nutrients or pumped with additives. Whole foods provide all the essential nutrients the body needs for the manifold tasks that keep us healthy and alive.

Whole foods provide us with complete nutrition. The macro- and micronutrients they contain are highly bioavailable – the body can much more easily digest, absorb and assimilate the nutrients naturally packaged in an apple or a turnip than those that are extracted, isolated and formed into a capsule, tablet or powder. While science has identified a number of essential nutritional elements such as vitamins, minerals, antioxidants and enzymes, whole foods contain many additional compounds whose roles have not yet been established. I truly believe that all the components are necessary, and they work together in synergy to help our bodies get the nourishment they need. When we eat a broad and varied selection of whole foods, there is no need to take vitamin or mineral supplements on a routine basis.

Essence

Whole foods – grains, vegetables, roots, legumes, leafy greens, lettuces, mushrooms, herbs, fruits, berries, nuts, seeds, seaweeds, fish, meat, poultry, eggs and milk – provide essential nourishment in the most natural and usable form, allowing macro- and micronutrients to be digested, absorbed and assimilated most effectively.

Action

Eat as many whole foods as possible and reduce consumption of processed foods. Do include fermented and cultured foods in your diet, as they provide friendly bacteria and enzymes that facilitate digestion, thereby strengthening your immune system.

Most commercially packaged foods sold in today's supermarkets have undergone an array of processes. Chemical bleaches alter the color of flour and oil. Harmful solvents are used to extract oils. Chemicals turn grains into instant foods such as quick-cooking oatmeal and rice. Hydrogen is blown under great pressure and high temperatures into plant oils to make them into products such as margarine and shortening that mimic the consistency of butter. High pressure and high temperatures are used to force whole grains through machines in order to change their shape and texture for boxed breakfast cereals. Preservatives are added to prolong shelf life. Chemical taste-enhancers, dyes and artificial flavors are added to make foods more appealing. Natural foods are refined until they become concentrated products such as white sugar, corn syrup and white flour, which are devoid of real nutrients. Dairy products, white flour, soy milk and pasta are enriched or fortified with artificial vitamins to make up for the loss of nutrients during processing. Animals are fed hormones and antibiotics that end up in meat, eggs and dairy products. Nitrates and nitrites are added as curing agents to meat products.

The intention behind most of these processes is to create a product that is commercially viable, has a longer shelf life and is at first glance more convenient and more enticing so that the customer will come back to buy more. Food corporations manipulate our food not with the health of the consumer in mind, but simply to ensure and enlarge their profits – some products are possibly even addictive. It is absolutely necessary to read food labels and to choose the purest foods available – foods that contain no additives or preservatives.

But food preservation itself is not a bad practice. Especially in temperate and colder climates where crops can

grow only during the warmer months, simple preservation processes have been in use since ancient times. Such methods do not affect food adversely, and some are even beneficial. The minimally processed foods that result can be considered whole foods.

Drying is one example. Traditionally, people all over the world have dried foods, such as fruits, grains, legumes, mushrooms, seaweeds, herbs and teas, even fish and meat.

Other examples are fermentation and culturing. Many traditional ways of preparing foods involve a fermentation process, as found in pickled vegetables, kimchi, sauerkraut, sourdough bread and fermented soy products like miso, soy sauce, tempeh and natto.

Fermented vegetables differ from marinated vegetables. Check the label – when the food contains vinegar, it is marinated; when it contains salt but no vinegar, it is lacto-fermented. Lactic acid, the by-product of fermentation, is a powerful preservative. Fermentation actually improves the nutritional value of a food. Fermented foods are live foods, providing enzymes and friendly bacteria – probiotics – that help the digestive system by enhancing the intestinal flora, thereby improving the immune system as well.

The same goes for cultured milk products. Yogurt, kefir, sour milk, buttermilk, sour cream and cheese contain friendly bacteria that have already broken down lactose for us. These milk products are much more agreeable than plain milk is to our digestive tracts. Most humans by age four lose their ability to produce lactase, the enzyme that breaks down lactose in the small intestines, and therefore many of us have adverse reactions to milk.

While oils are not technically a whole food, those that are cold pressed, unrefined and extracted without the use of chemicals or heat are in their most natural and desirable form for human consumption and are essential for good health.

Once you decide to choose whole foods over processed food products, you can improve your selection process even further: Consider how and where the foods were grown.

The best whole foods are organic. A food is labeled organic when it has been grown in accordance with the standards set by a country's organic certification agencies. Generally, these standards restrict the use of chemical pesticides, insecticides, herbicides and fertilizers. Organic foods cannot be genetically modified. Food animals are raised without the use of growth hormones and routine antibiotics – they are fed a healthful diet.

Scientific tests have compared organic foods with conventional foods in terms of nutritional content. Results have been inconclusive. My own conclusion is that there is no comparison between organic and conventional foods in terms of taste, texture and life force. The organic foods are far superior.

And the best organic whole foods are those that are grown locally – particularly in the case of fruits and vegetables. Organic produce found in your health food store or supermarket no longer comes from local family-run farms, as it did until the 1990s. Organic food production has become big business, and produce often travels long distances to get to your store. Produce from a distant farm lacks freshness, and its journey to your neighborhood has a negative effect on the environment.

So your first choice could always be the local farmers' market. Produce sold at a farmers' market is in season and is super-fresh – often picked that morning. Another benefit you derive from shopping at these markets is the opportunity to support nearby farms.

The best food source of all is your own garden. Food that you grow yourself is a gem, bursting with flavor and vitality. There is nothing as satisfying as eating salad greens, herbs or vegetables that you picked just minutes ago. When I put seeds into the soil, I always hold them in my hand for a little while to appreciate and infuse them with my own energy.

The Art of Reading Food Labels

Think of the packaging of a food – including the words on the front of the package – as advertisement. As we all know, advertising is often misleading. Its function is to make you buy the product, not necessarily to give you accurate information. Therefore, always read the ingredients list in fine print on the back of a food package to shed light on the real contents of the product.

The nutrition facts area on the package discloses serving size, number of servings per package, calories per serving, calories from fat and total fat. It specifically lists grams of saturated fat and trans fat, cholesterol, sodium, total carbohydrates, dietary fiber and sugar. It also lists major vitamins and minerals and their percentages of the U.S. daily requirement based on a 2000-calorie diet.

Some of this information may be useful. But for the most part, numbers in nutrition give only relative values. Daily vitamin requirements are different for just about every human being on this planet, and a food's caloric value can have varying effects on body weight – depending on what food it comes from, what time of day that food is eaten and whether the consumer has a fast or slow metabolism.

For example, a hundred calories from a cookie made with white sugar and white flour can set off a chain reaction that results in weight gain and cravings for more, while a hundred calories from a vegetable or whole grain are more likely to be transformed into sustained energy, satiety and no weight gain. Eating the cookie at bedtime can result in more weight gain than eating the same cookie at lunch because in the evening our metabolism slows down in preparation for sleep, while at midday it functions at its peak. And a cookie-eater with a naturally slow metabolism will take longer to burn the hundred calories than one who enjoys a fast metabolism.

The nutrition facts area also includes a listing of the product's ingredients, named in descending order – the first ingredient listed is the largest component in a food, the last one listed is the smallest component. It is this information that we really need to focus on.

Here are a few general rules about ingredients lists:

- The fewer ingredients, the better.
- Stay away from products that list many ingredient words you can't pronounce or define. Such words most likely refer to nonfood items, which could be any number of harmful chemicals, dyes, artificial flavors or fillers.
- Avoid foods containing curing agents, flavor enhancers or preservatives. Words and initials to look out for are nitrates or nitrites, monosodium glutamate (MSG), sulfites, potassium bromate, butylated hydroxyanisole (BHA), butylated hydroxytoluene (BHT) and tertiary butylhydroquinone (TBHQ).
- Always look for baking powder that contains no aluminum.
- Be suspicious of words like fortified, enhanced or enriched and of vitamins that are listed as actual ingredients. Products touting these attributes were most likely stripped of essential nutrients during processing and then supplemented with artificial nutrients to compensate for the loss, as in white flour and white-flour products. Be aware that artificial nutrients, produced in laboratories and then added to various products, are never an adequate replacement for the natural nutrients lost in processing.

Essence

Information labels on food packages reveal nutritional facts and ingredients. Reading the labels allows you to discern whether a food contains natural or chemical ingredients.

Action

Become a food detective and study labels carefully. Avoid foods that contain artificial additives. Clean up your pantry and refrigerator by discarding foods that list too many ingredients whose names you cannot pronounce. Play it safe – as much as possible, buy foods that do not need an ingredients list.

- Consuming artificially isolated vitamins – even those that are said to come from "natural" sources – is not equivalent to consuming the actual food sources of those vitamins. Only whole foods deliver vitamins in a form that the body can fully recognize. Artificial vitamins are simply not absorbed in the same way as vitamins that naturally occur in the foods that contain them.
- Be alert to sugar, a ubiquitous ingredient – not only in sweet foods, where you would expect it, but also in canned or processed vegetables, soups, cereals, granola, dairy products, soy milk, juices, nut butters and even salt. Sugar can appear as fructose, maltose, dextrose, sucrose, corn syrup, high-fructose corn syrup, glucose syrup, brown sugar, evaporated cane juice, raw sugar, Sucanat or concentrated fruit juice. (See the chapter on natural sweeteners, which offers alternatives to refined sugar – page 248.)
- Be wary of sugar-free and diet products. Sugar is often replaced with artificial sweeteners. They are serious neurotoxins. They can also play havoc with your blood sugar level.
- Don't be fooled by fat-free or low-fat products. They are often saturated with corn syrup to make up for the texture and taste provided by the fat that was removed. Whenever a fat molecule is manipulated through processing, the beneficial quality of the fat and the taste of the resulting food are compromised.
- When it comes to oils, avoid refined, solvent-extracted and deodorized oils. Unless the label specifically states that the product is unrefined, assume that it is refined. Avoid margarine, which is completely hydrogenated, and cheap vegetable oils, which are often partially hydrogenated – they contain health-damaging trans fats (page 43).
- Wordings like natural, all natural or whole grain do not guarantee a natural and wholesome food. Advertisements will pick up on the latest health and diet trends to convince you that a product is healthful and natural. When a label says whole grain, make sure that it says 100 percent whole grain or whole wheat. Many products claim to be whole grain, but the first ingredient listed on the label is bleached flour, and the whole-grain flour comes somewhere near the end of the list. This placement reveals that the product is made predominantly from white flour and only minimally from whole-grain flour.

Balancing Blood Sugar Levels

Carbohydrates have generated much confusion in the world of nutrition. The recent "low-carb" or "no-carb" trends are attempts to persuade us that carbohydrates are bad for our health. Of course, this is untrue. Carbohydrates are an important macronutrient that provides the body with energy. We need carbohydrates to make our muscles move and our brains work properly.

However, not all carbohydrates are created equal. Different kinds of carbohydrates have very different effects on the body and on the mind. In order to balance our body chemistry and moods, we need to understand the difference between simple and complex carbohydrates.

Essence

Complex carbohydrates – found in whole grains, vegetables and legumes – provide balanced blood sugar levels, sustained energy throughout the day and stable moods. Simple carbohydrates or sugars cause imbalances in blood sugar levels, ups and downs in energy levels and mood swings. When eaten in excess over long periods of time, simple carbohydrates deplete our body of minerals, compromise our immune system and set the stage for many serious diseases.

Action

Increase complex carbohydrates in your diet and reduce simple carbohydrates. Eat more whole intact grains, vegetables and legumes and fewer products made from flour. To satisfy a craving for sweets, eat sweet vegetables with your regular meals and have fresh or dried fruits as snacks. Prefer natural sweeteners such as honey, maple syrup, agave nectar, brown rice syrup, barley malt, blackstrap molasses and stevia to white table sugar. Avoid processed foods that contain added sugar, corn syrup (also called glucose syrup) or high-fructose corn syrup.

Simple Carbohydrates

Simple carbohydrates are actually sugars, consisting of one or two sugar molecules. Sugars are contained in various foods – there is fructose in fruits, maltose in grains and lactose in milk.

Highly processed white table sugar, also called sucrose, is extracted from sugar cane or sugar beets. Corn syrup, also called glucose syrup, and high-fructose corn syrup are highly processed sugar products made from corn. These forms of refined sugar are routinely added to processed foods.

When we eat a lot of sugar – particularly refined sugar – we cause a rapid rise in our blood sugar, also called glucose. We experience this rise as a "sugar high." Our body registers this condition as an emergency and signals the pancreas to produce the hormone insulin to counteract a potentially dangerous situation – too much sugar in the blood can lead to a coma. When our blood sugar level shoots up so high and so quickly, the pancreas overcompensates and sends a burst of insulin into the bloodstream. The surge of insulin then causes a drastic drop in blood sugar, and we experience a "sugar low."

Neither high nor low blood sugar levels feel good in the body. When blood sugar is too high, we might feel hyper, dizzy and restless. We might experience headaches or brain fog. When blood sugar levels are too low, we lack energy, feel lethargic, cranky or shaky and have difficulty concentrating. We feel best when our blood sugar level is balanced – neither too high nor too low.

Glucagon is the hormone that releases body fat to be burned for energy. When we eat a lot of simple carbohydrates or foods that contain added sugars, our glucagon production gets suppressed. So while we feed our bodies sugar, our fat stays put. That is actually an adaptive mechanism – the body wants to get back to a place of balance, and it needs to burn the sugar in the blood before it turns toward fat for energy. Those of you who would like to lose weight should make a note of that!

Insulin takes the sugar to all of our cells. We need a certain amount of sugar for our brains to work and for our muscles to move. But what happens to the sugar that we do not use up immediately? Part of it gets stored as glycogen in the liver and muscles, the rest as body fat.

As you can see, excess sugar is a double whammy as far as body weight is concerned. It prevents fat from being burned for energy, thereby preventing weight loss, and it gets transformed into body fat, causing weight gain.

Many foods that are high in calorie – nuts, for example – are also full of nutrients, so they belong in a healthful diet. Refined sugar is loaded with calories but has no nutrients. That is why we say it delivers "empty calories." It even depletes nutrients, particularly minerals, because the body needs minerals to digest sugar. Naturally sweet foods like fruit come with their own supply of supportive minerals. Refined sugar has none, so the body must dip into its mineral reserves in order to process it. In addition, sugar triggers the excretion of B vitamins and most minerals. So a diet high in simple carbohydrates will eventually deplete and weaken the body and set the stage for many devastating diseases.

Sugar literally paralyzes the immune system. For hours after it is consumed, it prevents white blood cells from performing their task of killing germs. It also curtails antibody production, interferes with vitamin C metabolism, causes mineral imbalances and makes our cells more vulnerable to bacteria and allergens. It can also hasten the growth of tumors because tumor cells are more effective than healthy cells at utilizing glucose – they can do more with less.

A high blood insulin level – the result of a high blood sugar level – is linked to obesity and high blood pressure, both risk factors for heart disease. Sugar is also known to exacerbate premenstrual syndrome, painful menstrual periods, yeast infections and candida. It is associated with depression, sleep disturbances and dental cavities.

Simple carbohydrates from highly processed and refined foods, such as white sugar, corn syrup and high-fructose corn syrup, are most extreme in their negative effect on our bodies. Unfortunately, these products are added to just about all commercially produced foods.

Biologically, we do not need to ingest sugar in its isolated form. Our bodies can make all the blood sugar they need from the breakdown of complex carbohydrates.

Fruits and natural sweeteners such as honey, maple syrup, agave nectar, brown rice syrup, barley malt and blackstrap molasses (page 248) do contain simple carbohydrates, but they are much gentler on the body. They are sweeteners that offer more than empty calories. They provide us with nutrients such as minerals and vitamins, and honey provides enzymes as well. Do practice moderation with juices from sweet fruits, such as orange, apple, pineapple, peach, apricot and plum. Juice is not a whole food – it is missing the pulp and therefore the fiber of the original fruit. When the naturally occurring sugars in the whole fruit are liquefied, they become too readily available and act in the body like refined sugar, causing a sudden sugar high.

Complex Carbohydrates

Complex carbohydrates behave quite differently. Unlike simple carbohydrates, they break down slowly. It takes the body a while to transform complex carbohydrates into simple carbohydrates or sugars. When we eat complex carbohydrates, our blood sugar levels do not increase suddenly and cause a sugar high followed shortly by a sugar low. Instead, the blood sugar curve is a gentle one, staying within the comfortable middle ground. Blood sugar levels remain balanced because sugars from the breakdown of complex carbohydrates are released into the blood gradually over an extended period of time, providing vital energy and stable moods that last for many hours. That is the beauty of complex carbohydrates: no extreme blood sugar or mood swings, but sustained energy and steady moods throughout the day. Foods that provide us with complex carbohydrates are whole grains, vegetables and legumes.

Exceptions to the rule are potatoes and fresh corn. The starches in these particular vegetables break down quickly into simple carbohydrates, so if you eat them without any other foods, your blood sugar level may peak. To prevent this, combine potatoes or fresh corn with protein- or fat-containing foods to slow down carbohydrate digestion. It is no coincidence that pairings such as potatoes with sour cream and corn with butter are traditional favorites.

Then, there is a group of carbohydrates that I like to call the "fake" complex carbohydrates. What I mean by that is white flour and all of its products: white bread, bagels, cakes, pastries, crackers, cookies, and white-flour pasta. In these products, the wheat kernel has been stripped of its outer layer, leaving plain starch and few nutrients. The starchy part of the grain is then ground into flour. Each tiny flour particle has a relatively large surface area and is easily broken down by the digestive juices into simple carbohydrates, acting in the body very much like sugar. Again you experience sudden blood sugar spikes and dips. Again you have to tap into your body's mineral reserves in order to process the food, because the food itself does not provide any.

Ironically, whole-grain bread has the same effect on blood sugar and weight gain as does white bread – because it is also a flour product. It is, however, preferable because at least it has all the nutrients that whole grains provide. Look for breads that contain some intact grains or seeds. There is a traditional German rye bread composed mostly of intact whole rye kernels and very little rye flour, which makes it an excellent choice of bread. The same goes for whole-grain pasta – it causes unstable blood sugar levels but it does contain nutrients. Just having some butter on your whole-grain bread or some cheese on your whole-grain pasta should slow down the blood sugar swing.

Many boxed breakfast cereals are touted as "whole grain," but there is a catch. Their ingredients were processed by high heat and pressure to produce puffed wheat, oats or rice. Some were extruded at high temperatures into little shapes or flakes, and some are flour products. Because the whole grain is no longer intact in these highly processed preparations, they can have the same adverse effect on blood sugar as refined sugar does.

Fiber is also a complex carbohydrate, albeit one that does not get digested. It therefore has no effect whatsoever on blood sugar. Digestible complex carbohydrates are tangled up and often enclosed by the fiber of the food. Fiber-rich foods such as grains, vegetables and legumes help to balance blood sugar levels by further slowing down the breakdown of complex carbohydrates. For diabetics who really need to limit their carbohydrates, naturally fiber-rich foods are saviors.

Since the 1980s, a measure called the glycemic index has been used in an attempt to show, on a scale of zero to a hundred, how quickly certain digestible carbohydrates in particular foods are transformed into glucose. Foods containing carbohydrates that quickly become glucose rank high on the glycemic index scale. The higher a food's glycemic index value, the faster the carbohydrate in that food is said to raise blood glucose.

Unfortunately, the glycemic index is misleading. For the purpose of creating the index, scientists isolated the carbohydrates in the foods they were measuring. But we never eat carbohydrates in their isolated form (except if we ingest a spoonful of white sugar) – we eat them as part of a package that includes all the other nutrients contained in a food. Any fiber, protein and fat in the food itself will slow down the transformation of carbohydrates into glucose.

For example, the glycemic index has unjustly given carrots a bad reputation. Carrots may rank high on the glycemic index scale, but their naturally occurring fiber and carotene have a balancing effect on blood sugar. The glycemic index does not take this into account.

More recently, the term glycemic load has come into use. It considers the entire nutritional content of a food, and it is therefore more accurate in predicting how quickly blood sugar levels will rise after the food is eaten. Fortunately, proponents of the glycemic load concept have reinstated carrots as our friends.

The Food-Mood Connection

Yin and Yang Foods

You are probably familiar with the Eastern concept of viewing life in terms of polarities or pairs of opposites – yin and yang. These polarities complement each other and form a whole. Night and day, hot and cold, light and dark, man and woman, contraction and expansion are examples of polarities. Life is a constant process of balancing itself out. If there is something too yin, we crave something more yang to return to a place of balance.

Food, too, has qualities of yin and yang. Yin foods are expansive, yang foods are contractive. Some foods make us feel light and uplifted, others make us feel grounded and assertive. These dichotomies are central to macrobiotics, a philosophy of food and life that points to balance in nutrition and lifestyle as the path to health and longevity.

As you can see from the chart below, salt is the most extreme on the yang side and sugar is extremely yin.

If you eat a lot of meat, eggs and salty foods, your body will yearn for sweets, alcohol or nicotine in order to balance itself out. When you have had a lot of sweets, your body in turn craves something salty. When I eat meat, I crave red wine or a dessert.

I remember an incident many years ago during a visit to Estonia with my mother. Although it was during the reign of the Soviet Union and there wasn't much available in the stores, our relatives and friends always managed to dish up the most amazing foods and desserts when we came to visit. One time, we had such a party at my father's house. First we had a variety of salty foods, then came the cakes, tarts, chocolates and cookies. After the guests had left, my sister and I started craving salty foods again to offset the overdose of sweets. So we began munching on the leftover savory foods. Once we got our fill of those, we were ready once again for some sweet treats. You can easily see why I always gained a few pounds when visiting Estonia.

If you eat on the extreme yang side, your body will crave extreme yin. Because you go from one extreme to the other, your body does not arrive at a place of balance. Instead, you continue to crave the opposite extreme and find yourself going back and forth like a ping-pong ball between extreme yin and extreme yang foods.

However, if you choose foods that are predominantly from the middle of the spectrum – some that are a little yin

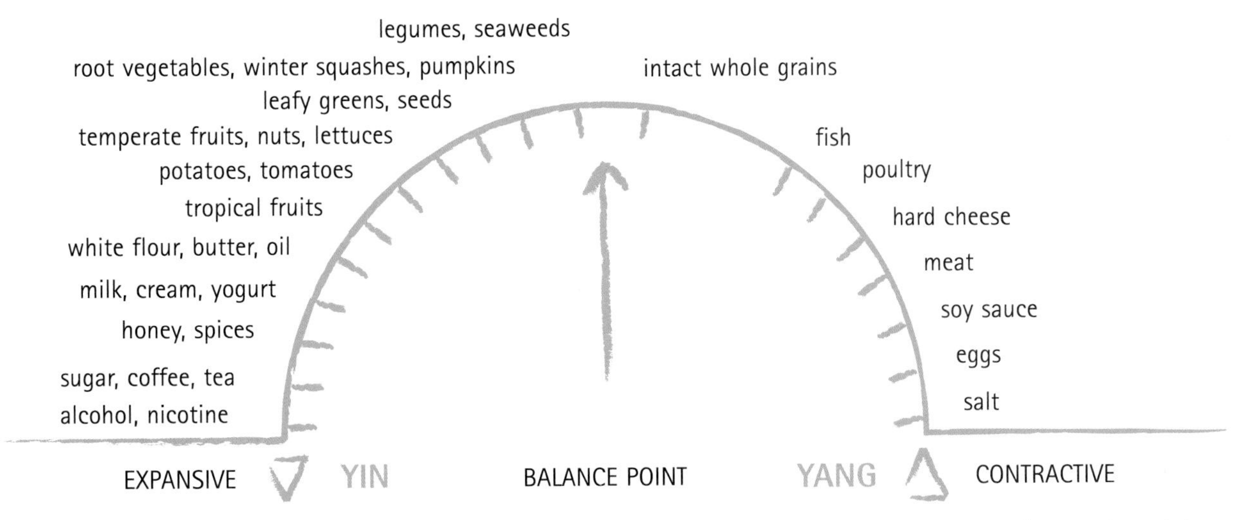

Adapted from *The Self-Healing Cookbook* by Kristina Turner (Earthtones Press, 2002). Used with permission.

Essence

Foods have qualities of yin or yang, with either expansive or contractive effects. Some foods make us feel light and uplifted, while other foods make us feel grounded and assertive. Eating extremely yin or extremely yang foods leads to a craving for foods with the opposite extreme quality.

Action

Eat predominantly foods that are slightly yin and slightly yang, not extreme in either direction. If you do eat extreme foods, balance them out with larger portions of foods that are moderately expansive or contractive. This will prevent a ping-pong effect and a state of imbalance.

and some that are a little yang – you will indeed feel balanced. You can stabilize your food needs as well as your moods by venturing no farther away from the middle than temperate climate fruits and nuts on the yin side and fish on the yang side.

Eating predominantly from the extreme foods can lead to fluctuating moods and physical illness. A diet based mostly on foods from the middle restores energy, alleviates stress and averts many diseases.

This is not to say that you should never eat meat. However, knowing that meat is very yang, you can balance out the meal by including a lot of vegetables or greens, which provide moderate yin energy. Have a smaller piece of meat and double the amount of vegetables you would usually consume.

Foods promote a yin or yang feeling in the body – and so do certain kinds of activities.

When we push ourselves too much, exercise too much or find ourselves in stressful situations, our yang energy increases and we feel contracted and tense. Do you see how we live in a predominantly yang world today? It's all about working hard, achieving, pushing our bodies and minds to their limits. No wonder we crave so much sugar these days.

To increase yin energy in the body, engage in any relaxing activity – for example, do deep breathing, practice meditation, yoga or tai chi, spend time in nature, engage in some moderate physical activity, take a bath or sauna, treat yourself to a massage or indulge in a beauty treatment.

Proteins and Carbohydrates

Foods that contain a high concentration of protein, such as fish or meat, provide the body with tyrosine, an amino acid that elevates dopamine and norepinephrine levels in the brain. These two neurotransmitters create a sense of stimulation, excitement and assertiveness, which can lead to keen attention, mental swiftness, fast reactions, heightened motivation and facility in overcoming problems and challenges. However, excess protein can cause stress, nervousness, panic and even violent behavior.

Quite the contrary is true when you eat foods rich in carbohydrates, such as whole grains and vegetables. Carbohydrates lead to an increase in the neurotransmitter serotonin. Serotonin is the feel-good chemical that makes us feel at ease and gives us a sense of inner peace. As the feeling of well-being rises, so does our sense of self-worth. Serotonin promotes good moods and helps concentration. It also allows deeper and more restful sleep.

You might choose to have some eggs or fish for breakfast when you have an important business meeting that day. You will feel more grounded, powerful, assertive and mentally energetic – ready to face any challenge.

When you need to study or concentrate for long periods of time or when you would like to relax and wind down from a hectic day, have some cooked whole grains and sweet vegetables. These foods will calm and soothe you, and because you are eating complex carbohydrates, your serotonin levels will be high for hours.

Isn't it wonderful how nature provides us with perfect foods for every situation? By understanding how different foods work, we can eat intentionally and make food our friend, not our enemy.

Essence

Protein-rich foods make us alert, motivated and mentally energetic. Complex carbohydrate-rich foods help us relax, raise our sense of self-worth and allow us to concentrate.

Action

Choose food consciously and purposefully. Plan meals that will best support your activities for the day.

Food Energies

There are many ways to think about food. Being mindful of what we eat enables us both to enhance our enjoyment and to make the most beneficial food choices.

In *Energetics of Food: Encounters With Your Most Intimate Relationships*, Steve Gagné describes how each food has its own particular character and energy. When we eat and absorb a particular food, we become a little bit like that food.

Each food has its own temperament – a basic nature that can change to some degree, depending on how the food is prepared and with what other foods it is combined.

Traditional Chinese medicine teaches us that all foods are a combination of either hot, warm, cool or cold and either dry or moist. For example, beef and duck are considered hot and moist, whereas pork is hot and dry. Buckwheat, too, is hot and dry. Butter is considered warm and moist, chicken and lentils are warm and dry. Red snapper and blueberries are cool and moist, whereas mung beans and raspberries are cool and dry. Trout and yogurt are cold and moist, lemon and parsley are cold and dry. There are comprehensive lists of foods and their ratings in terms of these qualities. But for our purposes, simply try to remember that meat is often warm or hot, fish is mostly cool or cold, grains are warm or hot and dry, raw vegetables are cool, leafy greens and seaweeds are cold, fruits and lettuces are cool or cold, spices such as hot peppers, ginger and cinnamon are hot. The coldest fruits as a group are citrus fruits.

With that concept in mind, you can make food choices that balance heat or coldness and dryness or dampness – both as sensations within our bodies and as conditions in our environment. It makes sense to eat fresh raw vegetables, lettuces and fruits in the summer to cool down. It might not be the best idea to eat a lot of yogurt on a cold, damp November day, because yogurt would intensify the coldness and dampness in your body. You might want to look for a warming and drying food instead, such as buckwheat. In the winter it might be more appropriate to eat a baked apple sprinkled with cinnamon than to bite into a raw and therefore cooling apple. For the same reason, the custom of eating a lot of citrus fruits in the winter might not make so much sense. Citrus fruits grow in the tropics, where their cooling effect is certainly needed year-round. It is preferable to eat citrus fruits during the summer. Vitamin C-rich foods suitable for the winter include parsley, Brussels sprouts and cabbage.

Foods can also be thought of as having a particular direction of energy. In the case of vegetables, it is easy to determine a particular vegetable's energy direction by observing the direction of its growth. Broad leafy greens such as chard, spinach, lettuce and collard grow up and out. These plants literally uplift and enlighten us and give us a sense of expansion. Narrow leafy greens such as kale, dandelion greens and onion tops grow up and in. They help us expel mucus from our lungs. Round root vegetables like onions, turnips and beets grow down and out. They have a relaxing effect and they help our intestines to absorb, assimilate and eliminate. They are useful for reproductive disorders as well as bladder problems. Long root vegetables such as carrots, parsnips and daikon grow down and in. They help us feel grounded and centered.

Another way to think about food is to sense where in the body the food resonates. All leafy greens, because they absorb the sunlight in order to produce oxygen, really resonate in the lungs, chest and heart center. We literally absorb oxygen and sun energy through these plants. Legumes resonate in the middle of the torso, and we can easily feel this after eating a bowl of satisfying bean or pea soup. Onions, turnips and beets resonate in the lower body, as they are beneficial for the intestines, reproductive organs and bladder.

Essence

We absorb the temperament, direction, rhythm and unique character of the foods we eat. Different foods resonate in different parts of the body.

Action

Experiment with different foods and notice how they make you feel. Discover how you can use a food's temperament to balance out a condition in your body or in your environment.

Each food also has a certain rhythm, a particular combination of speed and regularity in its growth. For example, cabbage grows slowly and evenly. It takes many leaves and much time for cabbage to form a head. Potatoes grow slowly with occasional spurts. Zucchinis grow quickly and steadily – anyone who has grown zucchinis in a garden knows that they grow at an amazing speed. Mushrooms and asparagus grow quickly and irregularly. Asparagus are known to shoot up overnight after a long period of seeming inactivity. The same goes for mushrooms – one rain shower and mushrooms literally pop up from the forest floor.

Besides these categories, each food has its very own unmistakable unique character. A chicken, for example, is full of active energy. That is one reason why chicken soup is so revitalizing and is used as a home remedy to treat flus and colds. For a person who is very active, talkative and nervous in disposition, eating too much chicken might push him over the edge. It might be better for him to choose foods that are calming and relaxing. A person who is shy, introverted or sedentary might benefit from the chicken's energy, as it might inspire her to jump over her shadow. Tuna is a fish that never stops moving. Even when it sleeps, it keeps on propelling. You might choose a meal of tuna when you are the one who needs to keep moving in order to get things done. Strawberries push their seeds to the surface. They might inspire you to express yourself more openly, and they might have a similar effect on your body. For some people, that might result in a skin rash. Legumes are supportive of other plants, as they release nitrogen, a fertilizer, into the soil. They are a compassionate food and might bring out compassion in you as well. Grains are very productive – a single seed can produce a wealth of new seeds. They support mental and physical productivity as well as fertility.

Next time you pick up any type of food, try to get a sense of its character. Look at it carefully and contemplate how it grew and what effect it might have on your body or mind. Have fun with this!

Cyclical Life

When observing nature, we can easily see that life is cyclical and constantly changing. Would it make sense to change our patterns as the seasons do? According to ancient ayurvedic wisdom, the key to living a healthy and happy life is to live in harmony with the cycles of nature. This refers as much to the seasons as to our body types and the rhythms of each day.

Seasonal Body Types

Ayurveda means "the study of life" and is rooted in Indian philosophy. It proposes that all manifestations of life come in three different qualities: *kapha*, *pitta* and *vata*. Kapha has the qualities of spring – the elements are earth and water. Pitta has the qualities of summer – the element is fire. Vata has the qualities of winter – the element is air. Body types also fall into these three categories. A person might have one dominant quality or a combination of two. Rarely, a person may exhibit all three qualities in equal amounts.

KAPHAS

In the spring, the earth is heavy from all the water of snow melt. It rains frequently, there is a lot of mud, and mucus and allergies abound. People who have kapha body types are big-boned and solidly built. They have strength and endurance. They do not need to worry about osteoporosis. They are often easygoing, deliberate and methodical in their activities. Their temperaments are even, tranquil and calm. Kaphas have slow metabolisms and assimilate their food with ease. They do not need to eat much in order to be well nourished. Because weight gain comes easily for the kapha body type, obesity can become a major health concern. Kaphas need to take care of their hearts – it is their weakest organ.

Kaphas do well eating an abundance of vegetables and lighter foods. Foods that have a drying effect (see the previous chapter on food energies) like grains are recommended as well. Spices are good, as they can break through congestion and stagnation in the body. Kaphas should go easy on oils and fats. Low-impact physical activities like walking and hiking work well for them. Kapha imbalances include water retention, obesity and congestion.

PITTAS

Like summer, pitta people are fiery, passionate, expressive, and competitive. Their physiques are medium-built and muscular. They love sports. Their skin is sensitive and has a tendency to break out in rashes. Their body temperature is high, which makes them sweat easily. Pittas enjoy cooling foods and drinks. They have an aversion to hot, humid weather and they are easily irritated. Pittas are leader types, enterprising and captivating. They make good public speakers. Pittas are prone to overworking and they burn out easily. They have strong appetites and quick digestion. They need to eat at regular time intervals and they don't do well skipping a meal. Their weakest organs are the liver, heart and stomach.

In order not to overheat, pittas should minimize hot spices and other energetically hot foods, such as meats – especially red meat. Fish and chicken are better choices of animal protein. Beneficial are dark leafy greens and sweet vegetables as well as whole grains. Lettuces and raw vegetables are excellent because of their cooling action. Pittas need exercise as a form of physical release on a daily basis.

Pitta imbalances include a hot temper with outbursts of anger, inflammations and burnout.

VATAS

Winter, the coldest season, is dry and windy. The wind can blow without restriction, as the trees are bare. Vata qualities are cold, dry, light, rough and constantly changing. The vata body type is thin-boned and slender, built with very little body fat. Vatas have quick and sharp minds and tend to worry a lot. Vata bodies are dry, which can manifest in dry skin and constipation. They have a speedy metabolism and a hard time gaining weight. Because their weak intestines do not absorb nutrients effectively, vatas need to eat highly nutritious food. Vatas especially need to nourish the nervous system, colon and bones.

In order to assist their bodies in nutrient absorption, they should prefer cooked vegetables, especially round root vegetables, and cooked whole grains, which also help with bowel function. It is advantageous for vatas to eat small portions of animal protein because of its warming and grounding qualities. Incorporating high-quality oils and fats is also essential, as they balance out dryness. Recommended are gentle, meditative and weight-bearing practices like yoga, tai chi and Pilates, which release nervousness while stimulating the bones to build up strength. Vata imbalances include constipation, osteoporosis and sensitivity toward cold as well as low stress tolerance.

After reading about these three body types, you probably have a good idea which you most identify with.

Essence

Ayurvedic wisdom suggests that there are three body types whose characteristics correspond to the seasons of spring, summer and winter.

Action

Experiment with eating and exercising according to your ayurvedic body type.

Seasonal Eating

Ayurveda teaches us to live in harmony with the seasons and cycles of nature in order to remain healthy. A proper diet is therefore connected to spring, summer and fall/winter foods. One easy way to figure out which foods are in season is to visit a nearby farmers' market. There, you will find only freshly picked produce from your local area.

Spring: After the cold winter and a diet of heavier warming foods, spring is the best time for a cleanse, using natural bitter greens like watercress, dandelion greens, arugula, sprouts and herbs like basil and parsley. These foods are most helpful in keeping mucus, congestion, colds and allergies at bay. Cut back on dairy, as dairy is a mucus-producing food. Turnips, radishes, daikon and the entire onion family are great fat-melters to help you lose some of that winter insulation. Eating less meat, fat and salt can be beneficial as well.

Summer: When the weather is hot, use the cooling effect of seasonal fruits, berries, lettuces and vegetables. Have more raw foods. Now is the perfect time for salads. Eat complex carbohydrate-rich foods to stay energized during the longer days of summer.

Fall/Winter: The autumn harvest provides us with nuts and grains, which are warming and most welcome in the cold seasons of the year. Meat, too, is warming and can be eaten in larger quantities. A little more salt is fine as well. During the colder months when there is not much sun, it is especially important to have salt because it stimulates the kidneys to produce vitamin D for calcium absorption. Prefer cooked food to raw foods, and eat warming soups and stews. Eat more healthful fats and oils to keep the body lubricated during this dry time of year. Eat vegetables that traditionally can be stored over the winter, such as potatoes, carrots, beets, winter squash and cabbage.

Essence

By living in harmony with the seasons, you allow your body to work with nature. Consuming less fat and fewer calories in the spring, more complex carbohydrates in the summer and more protein, fat and salt in the winter will greatly enhance overall health and well-being.

Action

Notice how your food cravings change with the seasons. Listen to your body and consciously adjust your diet as the seasons change.

Daily Seasonal Rhythms

While the cycle of the seasons is easy to observe each year, on a more subtle level, each day reflects a change of "season" every four hours. When we pay attention to the cycles of the day and adjust our lives to the flow of nature – specifically, to the position of the sun in the sky – we can experience an ease of being, feeling rejuvenated and energized instead of drained and tired.

From 6 a.m. to 10 a.m., we experience a period of spring. Our muscles get stronger and our body gets heavier, so this is the best time for physical work, exercise, gardening or house cleaning. Physical activity during this period speeds metabolism and gets our body into the habit of burning fat for energy.

From 10 a.m. to 2 p.m., we move through a period of summer. Directly in sync with the sun's highest position in the sky, digestive fire is strongest and metabolism is at its peak – a good time for a larger meal. In many cultures, people enjoy a robust midday meal followed by a period of rest.

From 2 p.m. to 6 p.m., fall/winter sets in. The nervous system is at its strongest, and therefore this is a good time for mental activity.

From 6 p.m. to 10 p.m., spring returns as our metabolism slows down and our body temperature drops in preparation for sleep. This is another good time for some light physical activity. Have dinner in the early part of the evening, so that you can finish digesting before going to bed. Allow at least three hours between dinner and bedtime. Dinner can be a lighter meal – possibly vegetarian.

From 10 p.m. to 2 a.m., summer is back, a time when the liver is actively cleansing our bodies. This is the time when the body takes care of repairs and builds new tissue. It is a good time to be sleeping.

Living with the cycles of the day means going to bed early – around 10 p.m., before the liver's cleansing activity kicks in. Ideally, digestion is complete by that time so that the liver can do its nighttime work effectively. It is best to be asleep as the liver detoxifies the body, filtering the blood and converting toxins into substances that can be excreted by the kidneys. When we regularly stay up late, the liver is prevented from doing its job properly, and toxins get stored in the liver and fatty tissues. An accumulation of toxins can lead to a number of health problems. I remember a saying from Germany, where I grew up, that was directed especially toward children. It confirms ayurvedic wisdom: "The sleep before midnight is the most valuable. These hours count double!" An early bedtime makes getting up early easier because our body feels lighter in the early morning after our blood has been cleansed.

From 2 a.m. to 6 a.m., the fall/winter season returns. We feel light, and therefore this is traditionally the best time for meditation.

Essence

Every four hours, the day shifts to a new "season." If we are mindful of these diurnal rhythms, we can be more effective in our lives. We can also be gentler on our body by conducting our daily activities during the most appropriate hours in the day.

Action

Bring a consciousness of the different "seasons" to your daily routines. Experiment with going to bed earlier and getting up earlier. Try having your biggest meal at lunchtime and an earlier, lighter dinner in the evening.

Proteins, the Dividing Choice

Protein choices generally divide people into meat eaters, pescatarians and vegetarians or vegans. Pescatarians eat fish but not meat or poultry. Vegetarians who include eggs and dairy are known as ovo-lactovegetarians, and vegans are strict vegetarians who eat no animal products whatsoever – not even honey.

I do not promote a particular philosophy on protein consumption. Instead, I would like to make you aware of the different protein sources available and encourage you to try them out and feel which ones resonate best with your body.

Why not be a flexitarian? How about being a meat eater in fall/winter, a vegan in spring and a vegetarian in summer? How about following a largely plant-based diet and having occasional meat, poultry or fish when you feel like it? It is a pity that many of us feel we need to put ourselves into a labeled box. In those days when I thought I should be a vegetarian, I would still succumb from time to time and have a little liver pâté, a favorite of mine. Although I did not have the knowledge I have now, I listened to my body and felt more grounded after that snack.

Many people have strong feelings about their food philosophies, and too often this leads to an attitude of superiority. Such people project that their way is the only right way and that everybody else is wrong and therefore inferior. We might have certain moral ideals as to why we shouldn't kill or eat animals. But sometimes our bodies do not agree with the thoughts in our heads. Some people might need some meat in their diets to stay grounded in this world. Some people might need a little animal energy to feel assertive and strong. On the other hand, many meat eaters would do themselves a healthy favor by cutting down on both the amount of meat they eat and the frequency of meat-containing meals. Too much meat certainly can pose a health risk – it puts a lot of strain on the kidneys and makes the blood acidic, leading to calcium loss from our bones and teeth and encouraging inflammatory processes.

To put it simply, carbohydrates are about energy, and proteins are about strength. A protein is made of amino acids, and different combinations of amino acids form different kinds of proteins.

During digestion, the body breaks down proteins from food into their component amino acids. It then reassembles them into customized proteins to fulfill different functions. Proteins are used to build and repair cells, tissues and organs. The body uses amino acids to build antibodies, enzymes and hormones and to synthesize hemoglobin, the protein in red blood cells that binds and transports oxygen.

Protein in food raises the metabolic rate and affects fluid balance in the body. It stimulates the production of glucagon, the hormone that allows body fat to be burned for energy – which is why high-protein diets can achieve weight loss.

Not enough protein can lead to sugar cravings, inability to focus, nervousness, tiredness, pallor, weakness, anemia and in severe cases, potbelly.

In one of her lectures at the Institute for Integrative Nutrition, Annemarie Colbin told us the story of a determined vegan man who goes for months with no complaints and then periodically gets very strong sugar cravings. He solves this dilemma by eating half a chicken. He then has peace of mind for the next few months.

Too much protein can also lead to sugar cravings, as well as constipation, dehydration, heaviness, weight gain, stiff joints, increased acidity in the body leading to calcium loss from our bones and teeth, kidney function decline, foul body odor and bad breath.

Essence

Proteins provide strength. They are the building blocks for our cells, tissues, hormones and antibodies.

Action

Experiment with the amount and kind of protein in your diet. Notice how your body feels with increased or reduced amounts of protein. Try both plant and animal protein sources.

Plant Sources of Protein

While animal sources of protein contain the eight amino acids that constitute a complete protein, all but a few plant sources are missing one or more of them. We can create complete proteins by combining foods deficient in one amino acid with foods that do contain it.

Legumes, such as beans, peas and lentils, are great sources of protein. They contain a fuller set of amino acids than do any other plant foods. We can make the set complete by combining legumes with grains. The combination of beans and rice is a perfect example. Among the legumes, **soybeans** are promoted as a most versatile health food, but they should be approached with caution. They do contain a complete set of amino acids on their own, so they are a plus in terms of protein. On the minus side, they are the most difficult bean to digest, and many people are allergic to them. But the most troublesome issue with soybeans is an antinutritional component that interferes with our ability to utilize or produce certain vitamins, minerals and hormones. All beans contain antinutritional substances. We can remove the substances from most types of beans by soaking or cooking. But for some types – including soybeans – fermentation is needed to destroy antinutritional factors. Fermented soy products are soy sauce, miso, tempeh and natto. Note that tofu, soy milk, soy nuts, soy granules, "soy meat" and "soy cheese" are not fermented. In cultures where tofu is traditional fare, it is paired with foods that mitigate its damaging effects – with seaweed to balance suppression of thyroid hormones, with miso to offset effects on vitamin B12 metabolism and with fish or meat to reduce mineral depletion. It might not be such a good idea for those who follow a Western diet to indulge in large amounts of soy products, especially the unfermented kind – soy is not part of the Western cultural inheritance. Tofu was never meant to replace meat or fish. It is traditionally part of a diet that includes animal protein. And for the same reasons you would avoid other processed foods, stay away from all heavily processed forms of soy, such as fake meat and fake cheese. Commercial soy milk is quite processed as well, and it often contains many additives. When buying soymilk, make sure it contains only soy and water. Most soybeans are genetically engineered. To avoid gene-manipulated soy, buy organic.

All **nuts** and **seeds** contain protein. Peanuts have an even higher percentage of protein because technically they are not nuts but beans – legumes. Peanuts can contain traces of a toxic fungus and should not be eaten in large quantities. Soaking nuts and seeds will improve their digestibility and make their nutrients more accessible for absorption by triggering the germination process, thereby releasing enzymes.

Grains and grain-like plants have served as the staple food in most regions of the planet. There are many grains to choose from: rye, wheat, oats, barley, buckwheat, rice, millet, corn, quinoa, spelt, kamut and amaranth. Grains have varying degrees of protein content. The most protein-rich are amaranth, oats and quinoa. Grains alone, with the exception of quinoa, do not provide a complete set of amino acids. However, pairing a grain with a legume results in a complementary amino acid combination that supplies the body with the complete set it needs in order to synthesize proteins.

Wheat, rye, barley and oats contain gluten, a protein that triggers allergies in many people.

Mushrooms are a good source of protein. Like legumes, mushrooms can be combined with grains to provide all the essential amino acids. But many kinds of mushrooms – even edible ones – contain naturally occurring toxins and chemicals that can interfere with digestion. Cooking removes the toxins, so it is best to eat your mushrooms cooked, not raw.

Seaweeds are surprisingly rich in protein. The amount of protein can be as high as 38 percent. Use seaweeds as healthful condiments sprinkled over soup, vegetables or grains. Add a piece when cooking beans – it will tenderize your beans and enhance flavor.

Nowadays there are many **processed protein** products on the market. As always, I advocate eating whole foods in their natural form as much as possible. Protein bars generally contain chemicals and sugar. Protein powder obviously is not a whole food, and I do not recommend eating it in frequent or large amounts. Definitely stay away from isolated soy protein, as it is an unfermented soy product.

Animal Sources of Protein

For me, the main issue regarding **meat** and **poultry** is not so much whether meat in principle is good or bad for your health. It is rather an issue of the food animals' quality of life. If the animals are held in cages, if they never see the sun, and if they are fed abnormal food, growth hormones and antibiotics on a regular basis, then they are not leading healthy, normal animal lives.

Factory-raised animals often endure unspeakable cruelty. This by itself is inexcusable. But extreme stress also ruins the quality of the meat. Meat processed from factory-raised animals is not a healthful choice for human consumption. It contains harmful chemicals and has a very different makeup from the meat of animals that are raised humanely, get to move freely, roam outdoors, breathe fresh air, bask in the sun and eat grass. If you eat meat, maintain good health by choosing only meat that comes from free-range grass-fed animals and poultry. There is also a phenomenal difference in taste between meat from factory-farmed animals and meat from free-range animals.

When it comes to quantity, try to eat a small portion of meat at a time. A portion of meat should be able to fit into the palm of your hand. Use meat as a side dish rather than as the centerpiece of a meal. To help digest meat, eat plenty of vegetables with your meal, especially leafy greens. These vegetables balance out the extreme yang energy of meat, and their high fiber content helps to move the meat speedily through your digestive system and to cleanse your intestines.

Experiment with different types of poultry and meat to discover what resonates best with your body.

Enjoy **fish** as a lighter source of animal protein. Wild fish caught in lakes, rivers and oceans are preferable to farm-raised fish. The overcrowded ponds at fish farms often have an insufficient fresh water supply, which can lead to an alarming level of excrement in the water. In addition, farm-raised fish are often fed inappropriate food, such as soy, poultry offal and hydrolyzed chicken feathers.

Also, be aware of mercury levels in fish. Most sources agree that king mackerel, shark, swordfish and tilefish retain the highest levels of mercury and should not be eaten. The following species are among those that retain the lowest levels of mercury and are safe to eat twice a week: anchovies, butterfish, carp, catfish, clams, cod, crayfish, flounder, Atlantic haddock, hake, herring, ocean perch, salmon, sardines, scallops, shrimp, sole, tilapia, freshwater trout and whiting.

Eggs are a wonderful source of easily digestible protein. Buy eggs from cage-free, organically raised hens. These have a more balanced set of nutrients. Do eat both the egg white and the yolk. An egg is a perfect whole food – just marvel at its harmonious shape and perfect packaging. It contains all essential nutrients to start a new life, all working together beautifully in synergy. There is no nutritional difference between brown and white eggs – the color of the shell depends on the breed of the chicken. But color does come into play when you compare eggs from free-range hens with eggs from factory-raised hens: The free-range yolks are much more intensely yellow.

While **dairy** products are a good source of protein, plain milk is a controversial nutrition topic. Many people do not tolerate it well and might show symptoms such as sinus congestion, post-nasal drip or bloating when they drink milk, which is a mucus-producing food. Many people lose the ability to produce lactase, the enzyme that helps to digest lactose (milk sugar), by age four. This fact might indicate that after the age of four we no longer need milk. Mother's milk is clearly a superb food for babies. But as adults, we need not depend on milk to thrive. The recommendations by the dairy industry to drink three glasses of milk daily is surely overkill. People of Northern European descent have the best chance at tolerating milk, while those of Asian and African descent do not do so well on milk.

If you have difficulty digesting milk, try cultured dairy foods like kefir, yogurt, buttermilk, sour milk, sour cream or cheese. Because of their friendly bacteria, cultured dairy products are easier to digest, and they also boost the immune system. We have all seen pictures of old yet strong and vibrant people who live in the Greek mountains and eat yogurt every day. They are living proof of the health benefits of cultured milk products.

Many people who are allergic to cow's milk find that they can tolerate goat's milk. Goat's milk has a higher percentage of fat than does cow's milk, but the fat molecules are smaller and are a better fit for human consumption. Goat's milk is also closer to human mother's milk, and a goat's body is closer than a cow's body to the size of a human body. Therefore, if you need a replacement for mother's milk, prefer goat's milk to cow's milk.

In either case, buy products from organically raised and grass-fed animals to avoid getting a dose of the hormones and antibiotics that are added to animal feed at factory farms.

Low-fat and fat-free dairy products are heavily advertised. The dairy industry takes advantage of the widespread fear of fat and cholesterol. However, it is important that we eat whole-milk products in order for our bodies to absorb the calcium these products contain – we need fat for optimum calcium absorption. Low-fat and fat-free milk products don't really make much sense if you are choosing them as sources of calcium because the removal of fat makes the calcium more difficult to absorb. In addition, they are heavily processed.

The purest form of milk is raw milk, which comes straight from the cow and simply gets chilled. It includes enzymes that help with digestion. The next best thing is pasteurized milk, which has been heated to kill off bacteria. Unfortunately, pasteurization also destroys the enzymes. Most commercial milks are pasteurized and then homogenized, which means the fat molecules are split so that they float evenly throughout the milk instead of rising to the top. Whenever a fat is manipulated, its quality is compromised. So if you can't get raw milk, try to find milk that has not been homogenized – the cream will be at the top.

Demystifying Fats and Oils

Fats and oils have been the subject of misunderstandings, misleading recommendations and hype for some time. The cholesterol scare has us thinking that animal fats are bad for us, that saturated fats are bad for us, that fat in general is bad for us. These claims are untrue. Some weight-conscious people fear fat for its high calorie count. However, the most serious health problem caused by fats and oils is from neither cholesterol nor calories – it is from rancidity and unnatural processing.

We do need some body fat to insulate us against the cold and to cushion our organs and hold them in place. We need to consume fat in order to absorb the fat-soluble vitamins A, D, E and K prevalent in greens and other vegetables. Can you see how a fat-free salad dressing does not do you any nutritional favors?

Essence

Fats and oils have different qualities, depending on whether they consist predominantly of saturated, monounsaturated or polyunsaturated fatty acids. Because butter, ghee (pure milk fat), lard, tallow, coconut oil and palm kernel oil are all high in saturated fatty acids, they are stable and can withstand higher cooking temperatures. Olive oil, high in monounsaturated fatty acids, is fairly stable and is suitable for light cooking methods such as sautéing, stir-frying and baking. Flaxseed, pumpkin seed and walnut oils are high in polyunsaturated fatty acids. They are very unstable and should be kept refrigerated. They should never be heated.

Action

When buying oils, always choose those that are cold pressed and unrefined. Organic butter is an excellent choice of fat, and so is first cold pressed olive oil for most of your cooking needs. Avoid all processed, refined, hydrogenated and partially hydrogenated vegetable oils as well as all products made with them, such as all commercially produced baked goods. They are harmful to the body.

Fat plays an important role in the absorption of calcium and therefore in the maintenance of bone health. It is no coincidence that both milk and cold-water fish come with a fair amount of fat in them – both are good sources of calcium. So fat-free or low-fat dairy products do not make much sense – we need fat for effective absorption of the calcium contained in these foods.

Fat also nourishes our skin, hair and nails and is important for proper brain functioning, especially in the developing brains of babies and children.

Too much fat in our food can clog up our lymph system and compromise our immune system. The right amount of fat, however, slows down the digestion process just enough to allow effective absorption of nutrients. By slowing the speed at which carbohydrates are broken down into sugars, fat helps to stabilize our blood sugar level. This actually fosters weight loss.

Another way that fats can help rather than hinder weight loss is through their role in the endocrine system. Our brain reacts to fat intake by producing a chemical called cholecystokinin (CCK). CCK stimulates the liver to produce bile, which helps in the digestion of fat. CCK also gives us the message that we have had enough food – in essence, curbing our appetite. A bit of fat in the diet hastens a feeling of satiety and satisfaction with what we have eaten, actually permitting us to save calories by eating no more than we need.

Our main concern when it comes to consuming fats and oils should be rancidity in processed oils. While spoilage in other foods is in some way apparent – think of rotten eggs, moldy fruit or even butter left out in the sun – spoilage in refined oil is insidious. We can't readily detect it because the product has been deodorized.

Some oils are more prone to rancidity than others. The deciding factor is the chemical makeup of a particular oil or fat.

Saturated, Monounsaturated and Polyunsaturated Fatty Acids

The building blocks of fats are called fatty acids. They come in three forms: saturated, monounsaturated and polyunsaturated.

The **saturated fatty acids** are straight chains of carbon atoms with two hydrogen atoms attached to each. Because of their straight shape, the chains pack together well and form a semisolid consistency at room temperature. Butter, ghee (pure milk fat, also called clarified butter), lard (from pork), tallow (from beef), coconut oil and palm kernel oil contain a high percentage of saturated fatty acids. These are very stable and do not become rancid easily. They can be heated to high temperatures without a compromise in quality. They can be used for cooking, baking, sautéing, and with the exception of butter, frying. Butter, because it is not pure fat, is not well suited for frying – its lactose and protein particles tend to burn and turn black rapidly. Ghee, on the other hand, because it is pure milk fat, does work well for frying. For the same reason, ghee is suitable for those with lactose intolerance. But regular butter is fine when heated in gentler ways. It is an especially good complement for steamed vegetables – add some at the end of the cooking process to ensure absorption of fat-soluble vitamins and enhance taste.

The **monounsaturated fatty acids** have one double bond between two carbon atoms, leaving the two double-bonded atoms with only one hydrogen atom each and causing a bend in the chain. Because of this bend, monounsaturated fatty acids do not pack together as well as the saturated ones do. They become liquid at room temperature and remain solid only when refrigerated. Olive oil is the most commonly used oil that consists of mainly monounsaturated fatty acids, but almond, avocado, cashew, macadamia, peanut and canola (or rapeseed) oils are monounsaturated as well. These fatty acids are fairly stable and are therefore suited for cooking, baking and sautéing.

The **polyunsaturated fatty acids** have two or more double bonds – two or more bends in the chain – which means their molecular structure resembles a semicircle. They do not pack well together at all and are therefore liquid even when refrigerated. Common oils with high polyunsaturated fatty acid content are made from corn, flaxseeds, grape seeds, pumpkin seeds, safflower seeds, soybeans, sunflower seeds, walnuts, wheat germ and sesame seeds.

Rancidity is the main problem with all polyunsaturated fatty acids. Light, air and heat affect their freshness and quality. Therefore, oils containing predominantly polyunsaturated fatty acids should never be heated or used in cooking. They can be used in cold dressings or sprinkled over cooked food when served. They should always be kept in the refrigerator.

FATTY ACID PROFILES

Saturated

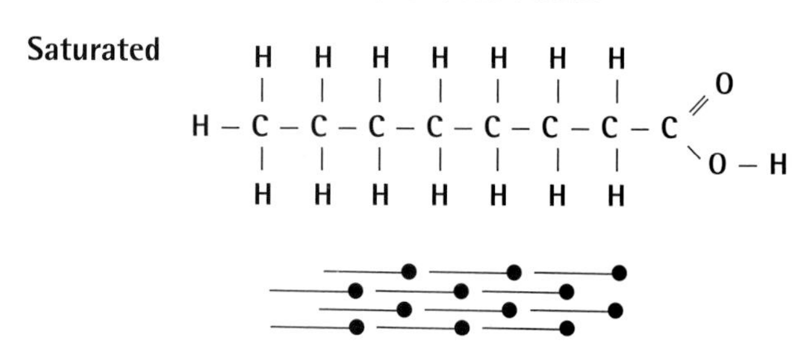

Monounsaturated

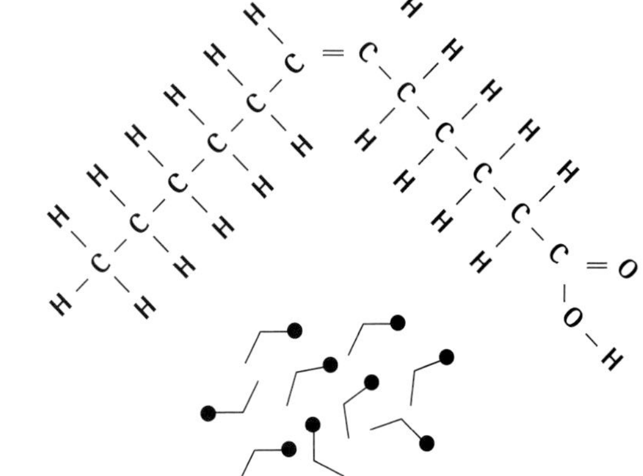

Polyunsaturated

Polyunsaturated fatty acids fall into two main groups: omega-3 and omega-6. These names reflect the location of the first double bond at either the third or sixth position in the chain. Omega-3 is very reactive and goes rancid particularly easily.

Omega-3 and omega-6 are called essential fatty acids because our bodies cannot manufacture them and we need to get them from food. Most of the polyunsaturated oils have larger amounts of omega-6 than omega-3. Flaxseed is the exception, with a higher proportion of omega-3. When it comes to the balance between omega-6 and omega-3, the best ratio for human consumption is 2:1. Too much omega-6 can lead to inflammation and blood clotting. Omega-3, on the other hand, is anti-inflammatory and blood thinning. Because of the recent overemphasis on polyunsaturated oils, many people are consuming too much omega-6 and are in need of omega-3 to return to a place of balance – hence the popularity of flaxseed oil and omega-3 fish oil.

Now that you have an understanding as to which oils are predominantly saturated, monounsaturated and polyunsaturated – and you can always check the proportion of each by reading the package label – you know which oils are suitable for cooking and which are to be used only cold. The chart on page 44 gives you a clear picture as to which oils are the most chemically stable and which are the least.

Processing of Oils

The highest-quality oils are called first cold pressed or extra virgin, and they are unheated, unrefined and sometimes even unfiltered. The name refers to a traditional method that is no longer widely used. Today, many commercially processed oils are "pressed" in a centrifuge. No heat is applied during extraction, so the initial process can still rightfully be called "cold pressed." But in a second step, steam and solvents are used to extract more oil from the leftover pulp, producing an oil of inferior quality. In the case of olive oil, this may be called olive pomace oil or pure olive oil.

Generally, high pressure, heat and chemical solvents are used to squeeze the oil out of corn, grapeseeds, safflower seeds and soybeans. Oils from these sources have high polyunsaturated fatty acid content, so they already become rancid in the manufacturing process. The rancid oils are then deodorized – with the help of more harmful chemicals – in order to be made palatable. To avoid this brew of rancid fats and harmful chemicals, stay completely away from refined corn, grapeseed, safflower and soybean oils. Remember: If the label does not specifically state that an oil is unrefined, you should assume that it is refined and that the polyunsaturated fatty acids it contains are therefore compromised.

Polyunsaturated oils also come from sunflower seeds, walnuts, pumpkin seeds, sesame seeds and wheat germ. If you can find unrefined, cold pressed versions of these oils, feel free to use them cold in dressings or simply sprinkled over your cooked food once it is served. Buy flaxseed oil only if it is contained in an opaque dark bottle and was kept refrigerated until your purchase.

Hydrogenated Oils

Finally, I would like to address the issue of hydrogenated oils, partially hydrogenated oils and trans fats. In essence, these are all the same thing. While hydrogenation is the manufacturing process, trans fats are the outcome. All hydrogenated and partially hydrogenated oils contain trans fats. Food companies wanted a cholesterol-free, easy-to-spread product with a long shelf life, so they began to promote margarine, a concoction made of hydrogenated oil. Partial hydrogenation is also used in some processed liquid vegetable oils.

Hydrogenation is a manufacturing process that uses high temperature and high pressure to force hydrogen gas into polyunsaturated fatty acids in order to solidify them. The hydrogen atom breaks into the double bond, takes out the bend and straightens out the fatty acid chain. The polyunsaturated fatty acid is thus transformed into a so-called trans fat. Now it behaves more like a saturated fatty acid and packs together well to form a semisolid mass.

But trans fats are biochemically incompatible with the human body. In fact, their chemical makeup resembles that of plastic. After hydrogenation, the original vegetable oil turnes into a gray, ill-smelling mass. This mass then gets bleached and deodorized, again with the help of harmful chemicals. As a last step, a yellow dye is added to make the product appear more butter-like.

The human body is unable to metabolize trans fats. They remain in the bloodstream and are likely to collect on the artery walls as plaque, which can lead to heart disease. Other conditions associated with trans fats are Alzheimer's disease, cancer, diabetes, obesity, liver dysfunction and infertility in women.

For decades, margarine has been touted as a health food, when it clearly is not. Today trans fats are in the news and have been recognized as a serious health hazard – in New York City, restaurants are prohibited from cooking with trans fats. Yet some medical professionals still recommend eating margarine over butter for heart health.

Fatty Foods

Besides the extracted fats and oils, there are plenty of foods that supply healthful fats.

Nuts and seeds and their butters (100 percent nuts or seeds ground), **avocados** and **olives** are good plant sources of healthful fats in the diet.

Dairy, eggs and meats are good sources as well. Whenever possible, use dairy, eggs and meats from grass-fed animals raised in a cage-free, free-range environment. If an animal has been denied access to the outdoors, sunlight and a natural diet, the omega-3 to omega-6 ratio in food that comes from that animal will vary unfavorably. For example, eggs from caged, grain-fed hens can contain 19 times more omega-6 than omega-3, as compared with a ratio of 2:1 in eggs from cage-free hens that feed on insects and green plants.

Cold-water fish such as salmon, trout, eel, mackerel, sardines and herring are good sources of healthful fats, especially omega-3.

Low-Fat or Fat-Free Products

Many weight-conscious people are buying low-fat or fat-free products. This might not be such a good idea. Whenever fat is manipulated, its quality becomes compromised. Because fat adds taste to a food, the fat in many of the low-fat or fat-free products is replaced with corn syrup to improve taste. For example, a low-fat fruit-flavored yogurt may contain ten teaspoons of high-fructose corn syrup in one serving! The calorie-saving effect of eating less fat is negated by the double-whammy effect of eating empty calories from corn syrup (page 26). When a food has little or no fat content, its sugars get released into our bloodstream even more quickly, leading to extreme blood sugar swings and accelerated weight gain.

What About Cholesterol?

Contrary to what some scientists and doctors want to make us believe, there is no evidence that the cholesterol level in our bodies is directly related to the amount of cholesterol we eat in the form of animal fats.

We make our own cholesterol, and it plays many important roles in our bodies. It is nature's repair substance, used to heal wounds and irritations in the arteries. It is vital to the function of the brain and nervous system. It protects against depression by helping in the utilization of serotonin, the body's feel-good chemical. It is needed for the production of all sex hormones as well as other hormones that regulate mineral metabolism and blood sugar. It is the precursor of vitamin D, which is formed by the action of sunlight on the cholesterol in our skin. It helps fight infection and is a powerful antioxidant that protects against free radicals, and therefore against cancer.

While a high cholesterol level in the body might be of concern, most likely the condition is not caused by the consumption of animal fat. Cholesterol levels increase under stress, as cholesterol is a precursor to cortisol and other stress hormones. Cholesterol levels can be high due to a diet high in hydrogenated or partially hydrogenated oils and processed foods. Therefore, it may not make sense to take cholesterol-lowering drugs before first investigating why your body is producing so much cholesterol. To lower cholesterol naturally, you might first try increasing whole foods in your diet while cutting back on processed foods, learning about stress management and incorporating exercise into your schedule.

FATS AND OILS: STABILITY AND FATTY ACIDS

Type of fat or oil and chemical stability	Percentage of fatty acid types			
	SATURATED	MONO-UNSATURATED	POLYUNSATURATED	
			OMEGA-6	OMEGA-3
MOST STABLE				
Coconut	91	6	3	-
Palm kernel	85	13	2	-
Butter and ghee	65	28	3	2
Lard	38-43	47-50*	6-10	-
Tallow	42	50*	3	1
FAIRLY STABLE				
Olive	16	76	8	-
Avocado	20	70	10	-
Cashew	18	70	6	-
Macadamia	12	71	10	-
Almond	5	78	17	-
Peanut	18	47	29	-
Rice bran	17	48	35	1
Pecan	7	63	20	-
Canola (rapeseed)	7	54	30	7
Sesame seed	13	42	45**	-
UNSTABLE				
Wheat germ	18	25	50	5
Walnut	5	28	51	5
Soybean	6	26	50	7
Pumpkin seed	-	34	42-57	0-15
Corn	17	24	59	-
Sunflower seed	12	23	65	-
Grapeseed	12	17	71	-
Safflower seed	12	13	75	-
HIGHLY UNSTABLE				
Flaxseed	9	19	14	58

* Although lard and tallow contain a lower percentage of saturated than monounsaturated fatty acids, they display the typical semisolid consistency of saturated fats at room temperature and can be considered stable.

** Sesame seed oil is fairly stable because its combined percentage of saturated and monounsaturated fatty acids exceeds its percentage of the unstable polyunsaturated fatty acids.

Acid to Alkaline Balance in the Body

The acid to alkaline balance in our blood has a major impact on our health and well-being. An overly acidic condition in the blood will set the stage for inflammation, demineralization and weakening of bones. We need an alkaline environment in the body for any healing to take place.

You might remember from chemistry class that acidity is measured in pH and that pH 7 is neutral. Distilled water has a pH of 7 and is therefore neutral. Anything below pH 7 is acidic and anything above pH 7 is alkaline.

Our blood is ideally at pH 7.45. Annemarie Colbin points out in *Food and Healing* that an acidic pH of 6.95 results in diabetic coma and an alkaline pH of 7.7 results in tetanic convulsions, both fatal conditions. Is it not amazing how the body manages to keep us in a safe zone? A mere 0.5 down on the pH scale will lead to death and a mere 0.25 up on the scale will do the same for different reasons.

Saliva varies in pH from 5 to 7, but we feel best at pH 7. The pH of saliva can change after just one meal. In the stomach, the pH is 1.9, a very acid environment due to hydrochloric acid, which helps to digest proteins. The pancreas is at pH 8. It releases alkaline enzymes into the small intestines to balance out the acidity caused by stomach acid.

Several factors have an impact on the acid to alkaline balance of our blood, including what we eat, how active we are and our level of stress.

Physical exertion has an acid-forming effect on our body. Under normal circumstances, glucose and oxygen combine to produce carbon dioxide, water and energy. During heavy exercise, the blood cannot supply sufficient oxygen for glucose to be converted into energy. Instead, in a process called anaerobic respiration, glucose is converted into lactic acid and energy. Lactic acid builds up in the muscles and can be felt as pain. When we breathe, the oxygen debt is gradually repaid and the lactic acid is converted to carbon dioxide and water, thus alkalizing the body.

Stress, too, has an acid-forming effect, and relaxation has an alkalizing effect. When we are under stress, the body initiates several changes in metabolism that are meant to rev us up for a spurt of peak performance: heart rate increases, blood pressure rises, stress hormones such as cortisol are released. Cortisol breaks down glycogen – stored blood sugar in the muscles and liver – into glucose or available blood sugar, which leads to more acidity in the blood. Relaxation techniques such as deep breathing can counteract the stress response by permitting the body to return to a calm and balanced state. The production of stress hormones stops, allowing excess glucose in the blood to be stored as glycogen and allowing the blood to return to its alkaline reading.

Acidic or sour-tasting foods are not necessarily acid-forming. For example, a lemon is in fact alkalizing. Meat and grains do not taste sour, but indeed they create acid in the body. It isn't until after a food has been metabolized that it will have an alkalizing or acid-forming effect.

Acid-forming foods include all sweeteners, starches and proteins, specifically alcohol, sugar, honey, nuts, seeds, fats and oils, flour, dried legumes, whole grains, fish, poultry, meat and eggs. These foods leave sulphuric, phosphoric and hydrochloric acids behind when metabolized.

Exceptions are quinoa, amaranth and buckwheat, which are mildly alkalizing, and millet, which is neutral. Almonds, unlike other nuts, are mildly alkalizing.

Alkalizing foods are fruits, berries, vegetables, green beans, fresh green peas, potatoes, seaweeds, soy sauce, miso and salt. These foods contain minerals such as sodium, potassium, calcium, magnesium and iron, which create an alkaline environment.

Exceptions are cranberries and plums, which are acid-forming.

Buffer foods are acid-forming yet calcium-rich. These include dairy products and tofu. Buffer foods balance acid-forming foods because of their mineral content and alkaline foods because of their acid-forming properties.

Traditional food combinations reveal our innate need to balance acid-forming foods with alkalizing or buffer foods: meat with potatoes, pasta with tomato sauce, oatmeal with milk, bread with butter or cheese.

How can we maintain our acid to alkaline balance? For most of us, being too alkaline is never a problem because if we eat too many alkalizing foods, we crave acid-forming foods. However, when we eat too many acid-forming foods – or when we are under stress or are exercising too much – we do not crave alkalizing foods.

If we fail to take in enough minerals from food, then our bodies pull calcium out of our bones and teeth to balance the acidity in our blood. After all, being too acidic is a very dangerous and potentially fatal condition, so the body in its wisdom reverts to extreme measures when threatened in this way.

Therefore, be careful to avoid a diet of mostly acid-forming foods. Always make sure to eat a healthy amount of vegetables and fruits when they are in season. Brothy soups are also very alkalizing. When making chicken soup, add a little vinegar to the cooking process to draw more calcium out of the chicken bones. After boiling or steaming vegetables, save the cooking water for a soothing and alkalizing drink. To alkalize your drinking water, add a bit of lemon juice or apple cider vinegar. Note that lemon juice has a cooling effect while apple cider vinegar has a warming effect (page 31).

Essence

Foods containing sweeteners, starches and proteins are acid-forming. Fruits, land and sea vegetables, cultured soy products and salt are alkalizing foods. Dairy and tofu are buffer foods.

Action

To prevent overly acidic blood, make sure to balance acid-forming foods with alkalizing foods, to breathe deeply while exercising and to practice relaxation techniques when you are under stress.

Why Do We Have Food Cravings?

We all experience cravings from time to time. Whether it is for your favorite kind of sweet treat, meatballs, pickles or hot chocolate, your body is sending you a message that is well worth deciphering. A craving is not necessarily a problem – it is a way for your body to let you know what it needs. Cravings might point to a particular nutrient that is missing in your food, an imbalance in your diet or lifestyle, an underlying emotional issue or simply a shift of seasons. If you view your cravings as clues to underlying imbalances, you can begin a dialogue with your body that could prove most valuable. You might learn a thing or two about yourself and gain a deeper appreciation of how your body works. Remember, your body is always striving to get to a place of harmony within, and understanding your cravings is a valuable tool for helping your body reach that place. In turn, your body is here to support you in your yearning for a healthy and happy life. Work along with it!

Let's look at some of the more common food cravings, what information they provide and how you can satisfy them with more healthful food choices.

Do You Crave Sweets?

Sweet cravings can have a number of causes:

- too much or too little animal protein in your diet
- a diet high in yang foods, like meat, eggs and salt
- stress, physical tension, overwork or too much exercise
- hormonal changes
- lack of physical activity
- consumption of caffeine-containing beverages like coffee, black tea and colas
- dehydration
- sleep deprivation

Try to please your yearning for sweetness with naturally sweet foods instead of indulging in commercially produced sweets that contain white sugar, corn syrup, white flour, hydrogenated oils and any number of chemicals, all of which can compromise your health. Fresh or dried fruit, whole-grain toast with honey and cookies or cakes baked with whole-grain flour and sweetened with natural sweeteners like maple syrup and brown rice syrup are some alternatives that are gentler on the body and the blood sugar energy curve (pages 248 and 249). If chocolate is your weakness, have chocolate that contains at least 70 percent cacao, which has proportionately less sugar or other artificial ingredients.

You might not think of vegetables as a source of sweetness, yet many – including beets, carrots, winter squash, fresh corn, fresh peas and sweet potatoes – do have a sweet taste, especially when cooked. Even an onion becomes sweet when cooked (page 220). Eating a lot of sweet vegetables with your regular meals will satisfy your desire for sweetness and reduce cravings for sugary, processed foods. Certain spices like cinnamon, nutmeg, cloves and cardamom can add a sweet touch to your foods as well. Once you start cutting back on white sugar, your taste buds will become much more sensitive, and to your delight, you will detect a lot of sweetness in your vegetables as well as in whole grains.

Do You Crave Salty Foods?

Most likely you are lacking minerals. This may be caused by an excess of certain foods in the diet or stress:

- refined and processed foods stripped of minerals
- produce grown in soil that is depleted due to overuse, monocultures and chemical fertilization
- sugar, nightshade vegetables (potatoes, bell peppers, tomatoes and eggplant), unfermented soy products, coffee or carbonated drinks – all of which cause minerals to be flushed out of the body
- acid-forming foods, such as sugars, starches and proteins
- stress can also cause mineral depletion and can lead to a craving for salty foods

Natural unrefined sea salt does indeed provide a host of essential minerals and trace minerals, so I recommend it for home cooking. Common table salt is refined and is stripped of most of its minerals in processing. Kosher salt, commonly used in cooking, is unrefined, but it lacks the minerals in sea salt. Mineral deficiency is very common today, hence the popularity of salty snacks. The irony, however, is that most salty snacks and salty foods sold commercially are made with common table salt and do not provide the minerals you need. Besides using unrefined sea salt in your cooking, eat lots of vegetables. Leafy green vegetables are powerhouses for minerals (page 131). Incorporating seaweeds into your diet is very helpful as well – they are the most mineral-rich foods on this planet (page 285).

Do You Crave Bitter Foods?

Cravings for bitter foods signal a need for help with digestion, elimination of excess mucus and detoxification. Reasons include:

- too many heavy, fatty foods
- too many different kinds of foods in one meal
- too much dairy
- too much meat
- too many foods containing chemical additives such as preservatives, dyes, artificial flavors, taste enhancers and traces of hormones, pesticides, herbicides and chemical fertilizers

Many people reach for coffee after a heavy meal to accelerate digestion. A healthier choice would be to incorporate leafy greens and herbs that have a bitter taste – like dandelion greens, watercress, arugula, mustard greens, kale, collard, parsley, basil or oregano – into your diet. All of these are liver tonics that support the liver in detoxifying the body.

Are You Dehydrated?

When you feel a slight hunger or drop in energy, you might actually be dehydrated. This can have several causes:

- not enough water intake
- too many caffeinated beverages – like coffee, black tea and colas
- too many alcoholic beverages
- too many salty foods
- too many dry and baked foods
- too many processed foods
- too many foods containing chemical additives such as preservatives, dyes, artificial flavors, taste enhancers and traces of hormones, pesticides, herbicides and chemical fertilizers
- loss of water due to physical exercise or strenuous physical work
- a dry indoor environment caused by central heating or stale air
- a dry climate in both hot and cold temperatures

As adults, we lose our sense of thirst, which is so prominent and evident in children. We might instead feel a mild hunger and interpret it as a craving for sweets, especially in the afternoon when many of us experience a dip in energy. When that happens, have a glass of water first and then determine whether you still crave food. Most likely, the water will flush away both craving and tiredness.

Are Your Cravings Seasonal?

Food preferences seem to change as the seasons change, and that makes perfect sense. In the spring, you might start craving green things like leafy greens and fresh herbs to counterbalance winter's heavier foods and guide your body toward a natural cleanse. In the summer, you might crave watermelon, cucumbers and lettuces, which all have cooling and hydrating properties. In the fall, you might yearn for baked root vegetables and roasted nuts, providing grounding energy. In the winter, you might crave pureed soups spiced with ginger to warm your insides. There is nothing wrong with these cravings – they confirm that you are in touch with your body as well as the environment.

Essence

Our bodies send us messages through our cravings. Most likely, they point to an underlying imbalance that needs attention.

Action

When cravings occur, pause and reflect. What is your body trying to tell you? What is the underlying imbalance? Deal with the issue at hand. If you crave an unhealthful food, substitute a healthful food that fulfills the need. Engage in a stimulating activity instead of eating to overcome boredom.

Do You Really Crave Something Other than Food?

Do you find yourself walking around the house searching for things to munch on? Do you open your refrigerator door to see whether there are any interesting snacks in there? Are you simply bored and looking for food to make life more interesting?

While food is deeply satisfying on more than one level, it will never fill the void that a boring life creates. No matter how much you eat, food will not solve this problem. Recognize the underlying reasons for your cravings and try to deal with those issues. Boredom indicates that you need to make changes in your life – to take charge and be proactive. Identify activities that will stimulate, engage and fulfill you mentally, physically and emotionally. Welcome creativity into your life.

We often reach for "comfort food" when our more primary needs are not balanced – especially when our relationships are not harmonious, when we feel lonely or when we experience fear. These food cravings have nothing to do with lack of nutrition. It is not the body that is hungry, it is our emotions. What is the underlying issue at hand? Try to deal with that issue instead of reaching for food to cover up, numb or compensate for a deeper need.

Make a list of all the things you enjoy doing by yourself, like reading a good book, listening to music, taking a bath, calling a friend, making plans for a dinner party, writing a letter. When you feel lonely, look at the list and see whether anything lures you at that moment. Instead of going to the refrigerator in search of food, engage in one of the activities from your list. Sometimes it is just a matter of sparking your interest for something else, and all food cravings are forgotten.

Are You in Need of Movement?

Everyday stresses, pushing yourself hard at work and spending too much time taxing your brain can put your body under a lot of pressure. Your body might respond by tightening up, feeling stiff or experiencing pain or constipation. In essence, your body is displaying symptoms of being too yang, and it craves yin energy to balance itself out. You may find yourself craving sweets and alcohol. While these will indeed give some temporary relief and will relax and numb the body, exercise or any kind of physical activity is a much better way to release that tension. Just a short walk in fresh air might do the trick. Step away from your computer and stretch your body. Take a yoga class, go jogging, dance to your favorite song, play ball with your kids – any physical activity that you enjoy will work.

The Art of Eating

Just as important as **what** we eat is **how** we eat.

Nowadays people eat under all kinds of strange circumstances – while walking down the street, while driving their vehicles, while sitting at their desks working, while reading the newspaper, while watching a movie. Eating is no longer something that deserves a dedicated setting or time frame. It does not call for our undivided attention – multitasking is the way of life.

But while we eat, we incorporate the energy from our surroundings along with the nutrients from our food. If we gobble down a meal in an unpleasant atmosphere, we absorb something unpleasant with that meal, while if we dine in a beautiful park or by the sea, we absorb something much more wholesome. Have you ever noticed how much more enjoyable it is to eat outside in the fresh air? How foods served at a picnic in nature are so much more appetizing? When dining together with other people, we also assimilate their temperaments and their conversation – as well as their neuroses.

Essence

In order to digest, absorb and assimilate nutrients most effectively, we need to be in a relaxed state of mind while eating. Chewing food thoroughly allows you to taste the sweetness of whole grains and vegetables, prepares the food for optimal digestion and boosts your immune system by creating T-cells.

Action

Take a few deep breaths before your meal. Focus on your food without doing any other unrelated activities such as watching TV or driving a car. Chew your food well, so that solids become liquid.

While there is nothing wrong with eating in company and having a spirited conversation, eating while discussing an important business move will most likely be detrimental to the proper digestion of food and absorption of nutrients. In order to get the most out of your food, it is best to eat while relaxed, unoccupied with intense mental work, and ideally in a pleasant environment. Pressure and stress can shut down the digestive system. Make it a habit to consciously relax before you begin to eat.

A few deep breaths will do the trick!

Chewing

Digestion starts in the mouth, as we chew our food. Carbohydrate-rich foods in particular benefit from thorough chewing. Saliva contains an enzyme called amylase, which starts to break down complex carbohydrates into simple carbohydrates or sugars while food is still in the mouth. As we chew, our food mixes with amylase, and the inherent sweetness of whole grains and vegetables gets released. Is Mother Nature seducing us to chew our food thoroughly by giving us a little sweetness in return? Very resourceful indeed!

The mouth is the only place in the digestive system where food is ground mechanically into smaller pieces. It makes sense that well-chewed food is a lot easier on the digestive system and is much better prepared for nutrient absorption.

But there is more to chewing than helping with digestion and assimilation. The physical action of chewing itself stimulates the creation of T-cells by the thymus gland. T-cells are the protectors of the immune system. Therefore, anytime you need more energy, healing, or strength – chew well.

You can even chew your beverages. There is a Buddhist saying: "Chew your drink and drink your food."

I like to do the following experiment with my clients, an experiment I learned from Lino Stanchich, author of *Power Eating Program: You Are How You Eat.* Take a clock with a second hand, fill a glass with water and have a seat. Sit with a straight back, close your eyes and assess your energy level at the moment. Make a mental note of it. Then, open your eyes, take a sip of water and begin chewing the water

as if it were food. Look at the clock and chew for one whole minute. Then, swallow the water. Take another sip of water and repeat one minute of chewing, then swallow. Take a third sip of water and chew for one minute. Swallow and assess your energy level again, comparing it to your level prior to chewing the water. You will most likely sense a rise in your energy level. It will be subtle but definitely noticeable. This is a great way to experience the power of chewing. When chewing water turns into a boost of energy, image what thoroughly chewing food can do for you! By the way, many a headache has been cured by chewing water as well.

Eating Out

Eating at Restaurants

One big difference between a home-cooked meal and a restaurant meal is that at a restaurant, you are giving up control over your food. You no longer know where the food came from, how fresh it is, how much salt or spice has been added or what kind of oil was used. You also do not know about the health and cleanliness of the various people who touched your food along the way. You have no idea whether the chef was in a good or bad mood, whether he loves his job or despises it. Was he rushing, or was he putting thought and effort into the meal? Did he prepare the meal lovingly or carelessly?

Sometimes looking at the menu is very confusing and quite overwhelming – there are so many tempting choices, and you get easily sidetracked from paying attention to your real needs and desires. It might help to check in with yourself before you even open the menu. What would you really like to eat? What are you in the mood for? What would make your body hum? Then open the menu and see whether there is anything along those lines, or ask the waiter to recommend something. Ask what the dish comes with. Does it include a good helping of vegetables? Could you substitute extra vegetables for the french fries? Could you have brown rice instead of white rice? Is the fish wild-caught or farm-raised?

I don't mean to imply that you should never eat in restaurants and should eat only at home. It's best to be flexible. Sometimes it could be less stressful and therefore healthier to go to a restaurant than to start making a home-cooked meal when you are running late and everyone is hungry.

When you are invited to a friend's house for dinner, welcome the food that has no doubt been prepared with love and care, even if it contains items that you would not consider health foods. Do not judge or reject someone else's food. Do not become the food police or a health food fanatic. You could easily find yourself being very lonely, cooking by yourself, eating by yourself, and feeling cut off from the rest of the world.

Sometimes it is preferable to go out, have a good time with friends, eat whatever your heart desires and forget about our precious dietary theories and precautions. Once in a while, some abandon could be more healthful than health food.

I would say that eating about 80 percent of your food as healthful meals is a great place to be. The remaining 20 percent can consist of whatever the circumstances call for. It is much more important to eat healthful foods most of the time than to attempt perfection 100 percent of the time. Our bodies can handle the occasional sugary sweet,

fried food or junk food – just not on a daily basis. And when you do transgress, do so with a sense of celebration and make sure you really enjoy yourself.

Eating on the Road

To avoid having to eat at restaurants or buy commercially produced food from the shelves of food stores, carry your own food with you. Take dinner leftovers with you for lunch the next day. Make your own sandwich with whole-grain bread. If you want to go vegetarian, fill your sandwich with a spread like hummus, made from chickpeas (page 218), with nut butters, roasted vegetables or slices of avocado. If animal food sources are part of your diet, have some hard-boiled eggs or egg salad, slices of turkey or chicken (choose organic and free-range meats and poultry), sardines, tuna salad or cheese. Top off your sandwich with a slice of bell pepper, cucumber or tomato and add some sprouts or lettuce. Take along some pre-cut vegetables such as carrots, turnips or celery. Cherry tomatoes also travel well. Pack a piece of fresh fruit. And always carry your water bottle.

Essence

Healthful eating is important, but it should not turn into an obsession. Sometimes, a meal eaten at a restaurant or at a friend's house might not be as healthful as you would want it to be, but the experience provides fun, relaxation, social interaction, communication and connectedness. These benefits may outweigh any imperfections in the food.

Action

Eating on the road is easy when you are prepared. Whether you carry your own food with you or choose to eat in a restaurant, apply the same principles as you do when eating at home: Be mindful of what you eat and choose nutrient-dense whole foods as often as possible.

Healthful Snacks

I learned about snacking when I came to the United States. Most Americans snack. I grew up with the idea that you would have enough nourishment at the major meals to last you until the next one and that snacking takes away from your appetite for real foods.

Some people do better with more frequent meals than just three a day. For others, snacking is a sure way of gaining weight, especially when the snacks consist exclusively of white-flour products and sugary sweets. If snacks work for you, then think of them as small meals. They should be nutrient-dense and made from whole foods, just like your regular meals.

Here are a few suggestions for wholesome snacking:

- nuts and seeds – buy them raw and dry-roast them in the oven to enhance taste
- dried fruits – mix them with your choice of nuts and seeds for a custom-made trail mix
- carrot sticks with hummus, nut butter or tahini (sesame butter)
- fresh fruit or berries in season
- a baked apple
- muesli – rolled oats, nuts and raisins or other dried fruits
- yogurt – buy plain whole-milk yogurt and sweeten it with maple syrup, fruit, berries or jam and add vanilla or cinnamon
- an avocado – cut it in half, sprinkle with lemon juice and salt or a little umeboshi vinegar
- a hard-boiled egg
- a piece of cheese on a whole-grain cracker
- vegetable chips – make your own by spreading thin slices of vegetables on a cookie sheet and baking for 30 minutes on each side at 350°F (175°C)
- curly kale chips – tear off bite-size pieces of the leaves (discard the stems), coat evenly with olive oil, spread on a cookie sheet, sprinkle with salt and bake for 15 minutes at 350°F (175°C)
- a green smoothie – combine one cup (240 ml) of water, four handfuls of greens (stalks removed), one handful of berries, one banana and one avocado (optional) in blender and puree

Getting Physical

Many good things happen for the body as well as the mind when we are physically active. Most people see weight loss as the main reason for exercising, but that is only one of the many benefits.

Physical activity fires up our metabolism. It allows all processes in the body to proceed more smoothly and efficiently. It supplies our blood with more oxygen, helps with detoxification, releases stress, circulates and increases energy, lifts our mood, makes us feel connected and focused, clears our mind, shifts perceptions toward a more positive outlook on life, increases vitality and makes us feel fully alive. The list goes on with health-enhancing effects such as better digestion, lower cholesterol, balanced blood sugar, sound sleep, mental stability, increased strength and endurance, improved immunity and stronger bones. People who are physically fit radiate power, a sense of presence and confidence. They keep active in many other ways as well, and they often enjoy a fuller life.

For many of us who spend our days sitting at a desk, working with our brains but neglecting our bodies, exercise is a great way to create balance and reconnect to the body, to physical sensations and to the grounding energy of the earth.

Essence

The benefits of moderate exercise are abundant. Exercise facilitates in all body processes, strengthens bones and muscles, releases energy blockages, combats depression and hastens weight loss.

Action

Identify a type of physical activity that you truly enjoy and do it regularly.

Several studies have shown that for greatest health benefits and weight loss results, low-impact exercise is best. Putting our body under too much pressure is counterproductive: If we exercise too vigorously, we shift into survival mode, essentially a state of stress – the body instinctively holds onto fat and does not allow it to be burned for energy.

Don't push yourself to a place of exhaustion. One good way to prevent that is to keep breathing in and out through the nose. When you start panting and breathing through the mouth, just take a break or slow down and get back to breathing through the nose. Once your breath has normalized, continue with your activity.

Regular exercise promotes muscle growth. Muscle tissue burns more energy than does fat tissue, so the more muscle you have, the more fat you burn – even when not exercising!

Weight-bearing exercises – walking, running, dancing and working out with weights as well as yoga and tai chi – are especially important for bone health. They strengthen both muscles and bones. When muscles are used with resistance, they pull on the bone and stimulate the breakdown of old tissue and the creation of new tissue in thicker, stronger and more flexible form.

Keeping our body moving and flexible keeps us feeling youthful and radiant. The yogis say, "You are as young as your spine is flexible." When we stretch, we also elongate the meridians, the energy channels in the body, thereby helping to release energy blockages and allowing energy to flow freely.

We have all heard the expression "runner's high." After ten to twenty minutes of exercise, our brain starts to increase the production of endorphins, opium-like chemicals that create a feeling of euphoria, well-being and optimism. Exercise is therefore a powerful antidote to depression. Aerobic exercise, including walking, stimulates more abundant production of endorphins, so it has a more profound effect on mental health than does weight training.

After exercise, our body feels energized and detoxified. With this clean feeling, we are less likely to want to eat

processed foods containing artificial chemicals, sugars and unhealthful fats. Our body will yearn for pure, nutritious and wholesome foods that support us in our journey toward optimum health and vibrant vitality.

What will it take for you to incorporate regular physical activities into your life? You might want to start simply by walking to the store instead of driving, carrying home your groceries instead of chauffeuring them or using the stairs instead of the elevator. A brisk walk in the morning or evening could be a great way to start or end your day. Taking a class in dance, Pilates, yoga or tai chi might inspire you to pick up a practice. It might be more encouraging to have a friend with you while you exercise or join a class. Experiment with different forms until you find something that you really enjoy and that suits your lifestyle.

Work and Profession

When you love your work, life can be very exciting and rewarding. Honing your professional skills, challenging your mind, overcoming obstacles, making a difference in the world, expanding your horizons, developing a new expertise, becoming a master in your field and seeing the fruits of your labor are all gratifying and nourishing aspects of your work.

So many people, however, do not like their jobs. Their work is not in line with their values and beliefs. It does not express who they really are, and it is neither stimulating nor satisfying. They hate the thought of going to their jobs, yet day in, day out, they do it anyway. They complain a lot but don't change anything. They feel trapped and see no way out.

Clearly, this lifestyle does not promote a sense of wellbeing. It can lead to cravings for food, when what is really needed is a change of attitude or work situation. In today's world, you can easily have more than one career – you can switch and start something new.

How Can You Find the Work You Love?

Here is an exercise used to help people find a more suitable job: Write down all the things you enjoy doing. Include hobbies, whatever fascinates you, favorite free-time activities, subjects you read about with great curiosity – make it a comprehensive list. Then, review the list and circle the items that are most important to you. Look at these topics and brainstorm on how you could combine them into a new line of work or career.

Essence

A job that you find challenging and rewarding can provide an important kind of essential nourishment.

Action

Find or create a job that you love. If that is not possible, then keep the job you already have and do it more lovingly – change your attitude toward the job and view it in a positive light.

How Can You Love the Work You Have?

Look at your work situation now and define what's missing, what could be improved. Take steps to change the situation. Instead of sitting back and complaining, be proactive. Stand up for yourself. Voice your concerns. Ask for a raise.

If nothing helps, then change your attitude. Look at your job from a different perspective: it pays your bills and provides you with the material goods you and your family need. Find all the positive points and keep those in mind as you do your work. Create some distance – don't allow stress at work to affect you negatively. Deal with problems in a professional manner, but don't let them enter your heart and soul.

Cultivating Nourishing Relationships

While the subject of relationships is huge and the scope of this book cannot do it justice, I would like to touch upon one essential aspect: the importance of cultivating supportive relationships. Unsupportive relationships, just like unfulfilling jobs, can lead to a hunger that seems to be about food but is really about something else entirely. But first, you need to determine which relationships are supportive and which are not.

I encourage you to examine your needs when it comes to connecting with other people. Are you more comfortable relating one-on-one, developing closeness with just a few good friends? Or are you a social butterfly who needs a lot of attention and many friends? What qualities do you look for in friends or partners? Whom do you click with?

There might be relationships in your life that drain you of energy instead of supporting you. Take a close look and decide whether you want to continue in these relationships. Sometimes it is healthier to end relationships that are not mutually nurturing and to develop relationships with people who are more like-minded. Take action and reach out to the people who share your interests.

Everybody can see how love, care, listening, understanding, comfort, touch, hugs, kisses, sensuality and sexuality can be very nourishing on many levels. Various people bring these nourishing elements into our lives, and we bring them into the lives of others. We often forget that relationships need time, attention, effort and even work. Make time to nourish important relationships – when they are harmonious and balanced, we are emotionally fulfilled. We do not feel the need to compensate with food.

Essence

It is important to discern which personal relationships in your life are supportive and which are not. Develop the nourishing relationships and de-emphasize those that are draining.

Action

Pick one relationship in your life that could use more attention or that needs some fresh energy. What can you do this week to blow a fresh wind into its sails?

Food for the Soul

Kundalini yoga master Yogi Bhajan used to say, "We are not humans who have a spiritual experience, but we are spiritual beings having a human experience." He also said that our souls come here with a purpose, and when we pay attention to and follow that inner purpose, the universe fully backs us up and supports us completely in our pursuits.

For me, spirituality is about belonging. It is about feeling at one with life. I enjoy having the sense of being an organic part of this vast universe. Spirituality means trusting the higher powers and energies that comprise our universe – and also trusting myself. On the deepest level, we are all one. Each breath we take connects our consciousness to the higher consciousness, to the universal energy or God. That is a beautiful image in my mind: our breath connecting us to God and vice versa, each breath reminding us of the divinity that resides within each of us.

Living in harmony with the universe can lead to finding yourself in the right place at the right time – in the same way that the stars in the sky go perfectly around in their orbits and in the same way that day follows night and spring follows winter.

Trusting the universe will open your heart and enable you to receive whatever you need – guidance, inspiration, love, acceptance, material support or spiritual sustenance.

I encourage you to slow down every so often and acknowledge that you are a spiritual being. I propose that you do something that feeds your soul and that you do it on a daily basis. Just as deficiencies in our work lives and in our relationships can be experienced as food cravings, spiritual hunger can translate into hunger for food as well.

On the other hand, food itself has a spiritual aspect. It is Mother Earth in collaboration with the surrounding universe that supplies us with food. What we eat is the result of joined forces: the light and energy of the sun, the cycles of the day and of the seasons, the water supplied by the sky and the earth, the spirit of the people involved in growing and caring for the food, and finally, our own energy used to shop for and prepare the food.

Spiritually, when we eat, we incorporate elements that exist outside of our bodies. As we chew, digest and assimilate these elements, we make them our own while deepening our connection with the universe surrounding us. The universe not only sustains us, it also contains us.

Essence

We are part of a nurturing universe that both sustains and contains us.

Action

Do something on a daily basis that feeds your soul: pray, meditate, breathe consciously, write in a journal, spend time alone, listen to music or walk in nature.

Lifestyle Suggestions in a Nutshell

- Every day, focus anew on all the positive aspects of your life. Do not dwell on your problems.
- Practice appreciation and express gratitude. This sends a powerful message to the universe, and more good things will come to you.
- Be generous. The more you give, the more you will receive.
- Sing or dance every day – that will bring you much joy.
- Laugh a lot. Every time you smile, you give your immune system a boost.
- Make a conscious effort to reduce stress in your life. Awareness practices such as yoga, meditation, tai chi or chi gong are very helpful.
- Practice deep breathing. Use it as a tool to calm yourself down, bring yourself into the present, refocus your mind and reenergize.
- Allow enough time for rest and play. Schedule some downtime into your calendar. Without proper rest, your body can not recharge, repair or detoxify itself.
- Pamper yourself: schedule a massage or beauty treatment. This is not a luxury but a necessity!
- Make sure you spend enough time outside in fresh air. Go for walks – even a ten-minute walk will make a big difference.
- Allow for time alone each day.
- Take care of your home. It is a reflection of you.
- Bring green and uplifting energy into your home and office by placing two plants in each room.
- One day a week, give your electronics a break.
- Avoid cooking with microwave ovens. Microwaving destroys the life force of a food.
- Nurture your important relationships – keep communication flowing.
- Place yourself and your family above work.
- Celebrate yourself!

Introduction to the Recipes

Well, now it is time to move into the kitchen and cook up a storm! In this section, you will find many tempting and very doable recipes. I aim to keep things simple, use only a few ingredients and streamline procedures as much as possible. I like to let the food shine in its natural deliciousness, not concealed with added flavorings or embellished with fancy techniques. I wish for you to fall in love with the natural flavor of each ingredient. You really can't go wrong – food made with high-quality fresh ingredients will always taste great.

My recipes are flexible. I encourage you to be creative in the kitchen. Experiment by substituting ingredients and coming up with different taste combinations. Many recipes will have suggestions for variations, but do add your own personality and flavor to the cooking. If you are not very experienced in the kitchen, I suggest you follow the recipes closely at first and cook the same dish several times until you become familiar with it. Then venture out and use my recipes as a base for your own creations.

Cooking does not have to be complicated. Practice makes the master. Did you burn your rice? That's okay – you learn from your mistakes.

All recipes are based on whole foods – no white sugar or refined salt, no refined or hydrogenated oils, no white flour. The collection of recipes is quite eclectic. Many are vegan, most are vegetarian and a few are based on chicken, fish or seafood. Most of the recipes have become classics at Polli Talu Arts Center, and I have taught many of them in my cooking classes in Estonia as well as America. Some date back to my high school years, some are versions of dishes my friends from other countries like to prepare, some are inspired by the Institute for Integrative Nutrition, some are new and some are old creations of mine. Because I have lived a big portion of my life in the United States, you will find some American classics such as Mushroom Barley Soup (page 184), Corn Bread (page 200), Pumpkin Pie (page 262), Apple Cranberry Hazelnut Crisp (page 264), and Blueberry Muffins (page 212). Because I am of Estonian descent, you will also find a few traditional Estonian recipes – Karask, a barley bread (page 198), and Rye Rhubarb Mousse (page 252). I have adjusted these to comply with the whole-foods concept of this book. When an original recipe author is unknown, I credit the person who keeps the recipe alive by preparing the dish and sharing it with others.

The passing on of recipes is a wonderful tradition. A recipe can move from friend to friend, from mother to daughter, from one generation to another and from one country to another. I would like to acknowledge and honor all who participate in the wondrous web of food making.

Although I try to be precise in all measurements, there are naturally occurring variations, such as the size of an egg or a tomato or an onion. In most recipes, the variations will not be a problem. In baking, it is more critical for proportions of ingredients to be exact, but in soups or vegetable dishes, the measurements are not so critical. Make a habit of tasting the food once in a while during the cooking process so that you can adjust the seasonings or other ingredients when needed.

Here are a few basics that apply to all recipes and may not be repeated in each case:

- All ingredients are fresh unless otherwise stated.
- Always rinse produce, legumes and grains, unless otherwise stated.
- Always discard the tough core parts of tomatoes, onions and cabbage.
- Onions are yellow onions unless otherwise stated.
- Onions, garlic and ginger are always peeled.
- Mushrooms are brushed clean rather than doused in water. Trim off any tough stems or bad spots.
- Leeks include both green and white parts. Trim off the roots and any tough green parts. Carefully rinse each leaf to remove any sand or soil between its layers.
- Salt is unrefined sea salt. Sea salt contains all of the original minerals and trace minerals that occur in sea water. It is tastier and more nutritious than refined white table salt, which often contains added dextrose and anticaking agents. There are several varieties of

sea salt, and some are more strong tasting than others. Be careful not to add too much salt – use just enough to enhance flavor without making the food taste salty. Always add salt toward the end of your preparation because it slows down the cooking process – especially for legume dishes.

- Olive oil is extra virgin, also called first cold pressed. Organic is preferable.
- Milk is whole milk, preferably organic and not homogenized. Raw milk is even better.
- Yogurt is whole-milk yogurt – preferably organic.
- Soy sauce is tamari. Tamari is a particular kind of soy sauce. It is traditionally brewed, and I find it much more flavorful. If tamari is not available, use regular soy sauce.
- Pepper is black pepper, always freshly ground.
- Herbs are fresh herbs unless otherwise stated.
- Lemon, lime or orange juice are freshly squeezed.
- Water should be cold filtered water or well water. Never use warm water from the tap, as warm water is not fresh – it has probably been sitting in a boiler for some time.
- Apple cider vinegar is raw, unpasteurized and unfiltered. In this unprocessed state, it provides friendly bacteria to strengthen intestinal flora and immunity.
- Vanilla is vanilla extract or scrapings of the vanilla bean. If those are not available, use vanilla sugar, which contains a small amount of white sugar. But never use any product that contains vanillin, an artificial flavor.

Many of my recipes originated in America, where a commonly used measurement is a cup. For European readers, one cup is half a pint, which is about 240 milliliters (ml). Measure out 240 ml and find a cup in your kitchen that contains that amount. Then, use that particular 240-ml cup whenever a cup measurement is needed. Or use a measuring cup that lists milliliters.

To accommodate both American and European readers, the recipes indicate temperature both in degrees Fahrenheit (F) and in degrees Celsius (C). They indicate measurements both in standard units used in the United States and in metric units.

Are you one of those people who thinks that time spent cooking is wasted? Think again. The best way to keep everybody in your family healthy is to provide home cooking. By cooking your own meals, you nurture yourself and your family on a much deeper level. You put your energy and love into the food. Your hands are the extensions of your heart. Practice mindfulness while cooking. Be fully present – notice the vital vibration that whole foods emanate and welcome the opportunity to appreciate them. If you can transcend any negative feelings you may have about food preparation, then you will come to consider your time in the kitchen as time well spent.

While you enjoy your time in the kitchen, you can still be efficient! Here are some tips:

- Cook larger amounts than you need for one meal. Refrigerate the extra if you plan to serve it during the next few days, or freeze it for future use.
- During the weekend, wash and pre-cut your vegetables. Store them in a plastic container or bag in the refrigerator. By the time you arrive home on a weekday evening, half of the preparation for a vegetable dish has already been done.
- Cook more grains than you need in one sitting. Cooked grains keep for up to a week in the refrigerator. Use them for porridge the next morning, in a salad for lunch or in a soup for dinner.
- Always cook extra potatoes. You can make them into potato salad the next day or save them for a weekend breakfast – home fries accompanied by scrambled eggs.
- Roast a bunch of nuts and seeds to keep handy as a nutritious snack.

So without further ado, choose a few recipes you'd like to try. Make your shopping list, buy all the ingredients you need, and try your hand at being a health-conscious chef! Have fun, be curious and adventurous, and enjoy the mouthwatering results of your efforts.

Breakfast Porridge

Breakfast is a very important meal, and it should not be missed. Breakfast revs up your metabolism and ensures that it performs efficiently throughout the day, working at tasks such as proper absorption of nutrients, accelerated brain power and optimal calorie-burning capacity. What you eat for breakfast will set the tone for the day. When you eat a meal that balances your blood sugar, chances are that all day long you will have sustained energy and stable moods.

Porridge is one great way to start the day. It provides complex carbohydrates that promote balance and produce a gentle energy curve, delivering sustained energy for many hours. Most porridges start as a flaked or rolled grain product, such as oatmeal, rye flakes, wheat flakes, barley flakes, millet flakes and rice flakes. However, polenta (coarsely ground corn), steel-cut oats (where the kernel has been cut into two or three pieces), kasha (intact whole roasted buckwheat), and quinoa can also be wonderful breakfast foods.

The method for cooking basic porridge is similar to the method for cooking whole grains. You may start the cooking process by pouring flakes and water into the pot and bringing them to a boil together – no need to boil the water first, as you are looking for a softer, mushy texture. Add a pinch of salt and a little butter or olive oil. Once the porridge comes to a boil, reduce the heat to its lowest setting, cover the pot and simmer for five to ten minutes. If you use an electric stove, turn off the heat completely as the burner remains hot enough to allow your porridge to simmer. For more taste and interest, experiment with adding cinnamon, cardamom, vanilla, nuts, sesame seeds, sunflower seeds, flaxseeds, almonds, raisins, prunes, dried apricots, dried cranberries or dried currants. If you want the sweet flavor of dried fruit to infuse the entire porridge, add it at the beginning of the cooking process. If you prefer a sweet taste explosion once in a while, add it just before serving.

Polenta and millet flakes are likely to form clumps. Therefore, when cooking these porridges, first bring plain water to a boil and then slowly and carefully pour the polenta or flakes into the boiling water while stirring constantly. Once you have achieved an even consistency and the porridge starts to thicken, reduce the heat to its lowest setting, cover the pot and simmer, stirring occasionally.

For steel-cut oats, I recommend the overnight cooking method. Steel-cut oats take longer to cook – about twenty minutes – and they like to splash a lot. So to avoid the wait and the morning cleanup, I start them in the evening. Bring the water and oats to a boil, add salt and butter or oil and then turn the heat off completely. Cover the porridge and let it sit on the stove overnight. At breakfast time, simply add a little water, stir and reheat. Steel-cut oats are great served with yogurt.

As you can see from the following table, most porridges are relatively quick to prepare. Check your porridge while it cooks – if it seems too dense, you can always add some boiling water to thin it out. Serve porridge as is, or with a little butter, yogurt, kefir or milk. If you wish, add a little honey, maple syrup, preserves, fresh fruit or fresh berries in season. I love oatmeal with maple syrup, rye porridge with lingonberry jam and millet flakes with raspberry preserves. Rotate your daily grain selections so you don't get bored with one.

Cooking Breakfast Porridge

For two servings	rolled oats	millet flakes	rye flakes	wheat flakes	barley flakes	rice flakes	polenta	kasha	quinoa	steel-cut oats
CUPS OF GRAIN	1	2/3	2/3	1	1	1	2/3	3/4	3/4	2/3
CUPS OF WATER	2	2	2	2	2	2	2	1 1/2	1 1/2	2
MINUTES TO COOK	5	10	10	10	10	10	15	15	15	20

Rye Porridge with Sesame Seeds

serves 2

This variation is one of our favorites at Polli Talu. It features the deep earthy flavor of rye with a curious crunchy surprise provided by the sesame seeds.

- 2/3 cup (160 ml) rye flakes
- 2 cups (480 ml) water
- 2 pinches salt
- 1 tablespoon butter or olive oil
- 1 tablespoon sesame seeds (raw or roasted)

1. Combine the rye flakes, water, salt and butter in a pot and bring to a boil.
2. Reduce the heat to its lowest setting and simmer for 5 to 10 minutes.
3. Stir in the sesame seeds.

Serve topped with a pat of butter and spoonful of lingonberry jam.

Multigrain Porridge with Berries

serves 2

This recipe uses a mixture of oat, rye, wheat and barley flakes. At Polli Talu, we love to add freshly picked currants in the summer – the porridge becomes a feast for the eyes as well as the taste buds. Soften the tartness of the berries with a little honey.

1 cup (240 ml) multigrain flakes
2 cups (480 ml) water
2 pinches salt
1 tablespoon butter or olive oil
½ cup (120 ml) berries (currants, raspberries, blueberries or strawberries)

1. Combine the flakes, water, salt and butter in a pot and bring to a boil.
2. Reduce the heat to its lowest setting and simmer for 5 to 10 minutes.
3. Divide the porridge into serving bowls and top with berries.

Serve topped with a pat of butter and a drizzle of honey.

Vegetables

Vegetables are a great source of complex carbohydrates, including micronutrients in the form of vitamins and minerals and in the form of protective phytochemicals – compounds that strengthen our natural defenses against disease. Antioxidants are one class of phytochemicals that can block the actions of so-called free radicals – highly reactive chemical compounds that can damage tissues and alter the genetic code contained in our cells, promoting cancer and premature aging. Most antioxidants are actually pigments, so choose intensely colored vegetables for highest antioxidant content. When you eat a variety of vegetables, you can be sure to cover your entire vitamin, mineral and phytochemical needs.

Vegetables deserve a much more prominent role at the table than they have been granted. Make vegetables your centerpiece: When arranging food on your plate, cover half the plate with vegetables, a quarter of the plate with grains and the remaining quarter with protein-rich foods such as meat, fish, eggs or legumes. I have fallen in love with vegetables over the years, and I yearn for them at every meal.

Vegetables are very low in calorie. If you are trying to lose weight, load up on the vegetables – eat as many as you want. The feeling of fullness that they provide will enable you to cut back on higher-calorie foods. This is a simple recipe for weight loss that does not involve deprivation or meager portions.

There is one group of vegetables that you need to be a little cautious of. Tomatoes, potatoes, peppers and eggplant belong to the group called nightshade vegetables. They contain alkaloids, which can leach calcium out of your bones. Eat these in moderation.

Remember the particular energies and properties of vegetables from the chapter on food energies (page 31)? Long roots provide us with grounding and centering energy. Round roots help us to absorb, assimilate and elimnate. Leafy greens provide uplifting energy. Try to have vegetables from each type on a daily basis.

Whenever I eat vegetables, I feel deeply nourished and oh so satisfied – sometimes I even have them for breakfast. And there is such an abundance of varieties to choose from! What is your favorite vegetable?

Five basic ways to prepare vegetables are steaming, boiling, stir-frying or sautéing, baking and mashing.

To steam vegetables, cut them into bite-size pieces. Place root vegetables, such as beets, carrots and rutabagas, at the bottom of your steamer basket. Add enough water to fill the space below the basket and bring the water to a boil. Gradually add the more tender vegetables such as zucchini or other squashes, green beans, broccoli or leafy greens, which need less time to steam. Wait a few minutes before layering on each vegetable. Check for softness and adjust the cooking time to your liking. Root vegetables might take anywhere from ten to twenty minutes, while vegetables that grow above the earth might take five to ten minutes. Steaming vegetables will leave them fibrous, so it is a good cooking method for those trying to lose weight.

Boiling is another quick way to prepare vegetables. Bring about two inches of water to a boil. Add the vegetables, and if you like, a little salt. Continue to boil over medium heat. Again, root vegetables will take longer to soften than others. Check for softness and color – when you cook green vegetables, remove them from the heat while they are still vibrantly green. In that state, they deliver the best taste experience. Once they turn olive green, much of the flavor is lost. The same goes for softness – root vegetables should be soft enough to lose their raw taste but not their native flavor.

When making steamed or boiled vegetables, always reserve the cooking liquid. Drink it as a soothing and alkalizing beverage. You'll be surprised how lovely and sweet it tastes. Or save it in the refrigerator for up to a week to use when cooking soups or whole grains.

You can serve steamed or boiled vegetables plain or enhance their flavor by adding a dressing, fresh herbs, roasted nuts or seeds, oil or butter, soy sauce or simply a squeeze of lemon juice. I am amazed anew each time I taste what a little lemon juice can do to enliven the flavor of vegetables. Plus, lemon is beneficial for calcium assimilation. And some fat in the form of oil or butter helps with the absorption of fat-soluble vitamins in your vegetables.

Stir-frying or sautéing are quick and tasty ways to prepare vegetables. Cut the vegetables into thin pieces. Heat a little olive oil in a pan or wok, add some garlic slices or chopped ginger if you like, then add the vegetables. Again, start with root vegetables, followed by the more tender varieties. Stir the vegetables so that they all get a light coating of oil, which will seal in their flavor. You can add a little water to create a steaming action in your stir-fry, which will speed up the cooking process. In that case, cover your pan or wok and let the vegetables steam for a few minutes. When the vegetables reach the desired softness, add some salt or soy sauce. Some of my favorite vegetables for stir-frying are combinations of broccoli, onions, carrots, pak choy and red bell peppers.

In recipes that call for onions and other vegetables to be sautéed and then added to a soup or other dish, be sure to transfer every bit of the good flavor from the pan after you have removed the onion mixture – add a little water to the pan, reheat, stir and pour in this sauté residue.

Baking vegetables takes a bit longer, but once they are in the oven, your work is done. Because the baking process removes moisture, it intensifies a vegetable's flavor. Experiment with different kinds, but if you combine several in a single dish, select vegetables from the same group so that their baking times will be comparable. For example, combine a variety of root vegetables, or pair broccoli with cauliflower. Preheat the oven to 425°F (225°C). To prepare the vegetables for baking, cut them into bite-size pieces, florets or sticklike shapes, place them on a cookie sheet and sprinkle with olive oil. Handle each piece to ensure that it is coated with oil. Arrange the pieces evenly on the sheet and bake for thirty to sixty minutes. To add some more flavor, sprinkle with herbs such as thyme or rosemary before baking. When the vegetables have reached the desired softness, remove them from the oven and sprinkle with a little salt. Great vegetables to bake are carrots, green beans, rutabagas (which I cut into rectangular pieces, each about two inches (5 cm) long and a half-inch (1 cm) thick), Brussels sprouts (cut in half) and sweet potatoes (I bake them whole in their skins and serve them with a little butter and lime juice – they are divine!).

Mashing is a nice variation, not only for potatoes but for other root vegetables as well. Carrots, sweet potatoes, turnips and rutabagas are great candidates, either solo or in combination. First, steam or boil the vegetables until they are quite soft. Pour off the cooking liquid and save it. With a potato masher, work the vegetables into an even mash. Add some of the cooking liquid for creaminess. An alternate method is to puree the vegetables in your blender or food processor. Add some butter or olive oil and dried herbs like tarragon, thyme or rosemary or finely chopped fresh herbs like parsley or basil. Some pressed garlic will give your mashed roots a nice kick.

Leftover vegetables can easily be turned into a delicious vinaigrette (page 230). Or you can add them to green salads and grain salads, mix them into a quiche (page 204) or bake them in a frittata (page 208).

Mushrooms

A mushroom is the fruit of a fungus and is thus related to mold and yeast. Some sources consider a mushroom to be in between a plant and an animal. The cell walls of mushrooms are composed of chitin, which is the same compound that is found in the outer skeletons of crustaceans and insects.

The medicinal value of a mushroom lies in its ability to detoxify the body. A mushroom feeds on organic matter – decaying wood is a favorite food source. After we consume mushrooms, they continue to absorb organic matter, including toxins. They manage to safely eliminate unfriendly bacteria from the digestive tract, fat from the blood and excess mucus from the lungs. Mushrooms have traditionally been paired with meat dishes, because they keep at bay any bacteria that might have developed on the meat.

Mushrooms have high protein content, and they also provide ample vitamin B2 and zinc. Because of their glutamic acid content, mushrooms act as a taste enhancer for all savory foods they are cooked with.

Mushrooms are earthy, mysterious and delicious. I remember vividly my first encounter with deep black trumpet mushrooms at a farmers' market in Helsinki. I had never seen anything like them. Their shape and intense color pulled me in and I just had to buy them and try them out. Their flavor was unbelievably sweet and rich. Eating them was an unforgettable experience for the senses. I never saw them again.

Wild mushrooms are much more flavorful than commercially grown mushrooms. Some people have extensive knowledge of mushrooms and enjoy gathering the edible kinds in the forest after a rainfall, when these fungus fruits literally pop into existence. Please do not attempt to forage for mushrooms unless you know what you are doing or are accompanied by an expert. Many varieties of mushrooms that look very appetizing are in fact poisonous.

Mushrooms can be dried and kept for a long time. To rehydrate them, soak them in water for at least 20 minutes or even overnight. Dried mushrooms expand to about eight times their dried volume. Other methods of preservation include salting, marinating and lacto-fermenting.

Mushrooms are best eaten cooked, as certain carcinogenic chemicals in the raw mushroom are neutralized in heating. Find mushrooms in recipes on pages 88, 110, 126, 146, 184 and 206.

Vegetable Recipes

Steamed Vegetables with Lemon Soy Dressing

serves 6

What makes this dish a winner is the dressing. I learned to make this dressing from my friend and colleague choreographer Muna Tseng, who was born in Hong Kong.

Dressing:

2 cloves garlic, pressed
1 piece fresh ginger, about 1½ inches (4 cm), peeled and chopped fine
juice of 2 lemons
¼ cup (60 ml) olive oil
¼ cup (60 ml) soy sauce
1 tablespoon snipped chives, optional

Vegetables:

2 red beets
3 carrots — all peeled, cut into bite-size pieces
1 turnip
1 cauliflower, separated into florets
1 leek, cut into ½-inch (1-cm) pieces
1 can (15 ounces or 420 g) chickpeas, drained and rinsed
6 leaves kale, stalks removed, torn into bite-size pieces
a few cilantro leaves

1. Combine the dressing ingredients in a glass jar. Close the lid and shake to mix.
2. Fill a pot with 1 inch (2½ cm) of water, insert a steamer basket and bring the water to a boil. Add the vegetables – start with the beets, then add the carrots, then the turnip, then the cauliflower – waiting three minutes after each addition. Follow with the leek, chickpeas and kale, added at once. Steam until tender.

Serve on a bed of cooked brown rice - spoon the rice on individual plates, then top with the vegetables. Pour on the dressing and garnish with cilantro leaves.

Red Cabbage with Carrots

serves 6

A colorful medley of vegetables with a little spiciness from the fresh red hot pepper and garlic.

1 medium onion, chopped
2 tablespoons olive oil
1 small red cabbage, cut into strips
3 carrots, cut into rounds
1 to 2 tablespoons apple cider vinegar
1 fresh red hot pepper, cut into thin rings
2 cloves garlic, pressed
1 bunch scallions, chopped
salt
a few parsley leaves

1. In a large pan or pot, sauté the onion in the oil until golden.
2. Add the cabbage, carrots and a little water. Cover and simmer until the carrots and cabbage are soft, about 10 minutes.
3. Add the vinegar, hot pepper, garlic and scallions. Add salt to taste and simmer for another 2 minutes.

Serve hot, garnished with parsley.

Note: Adding the garlic at the last stages of cooking will give the dish a nice kick. If you prefer less intensity, add the garlic along with the cabbage and carrots.

Zucchini Tomato Casserole

serves 8 to 10

A light summer meal – prepare it when zucchinis and tomatoes are in season.

2 large or 3 small zucchinis, cut into rounds
18 ounces (500 g) feta, cut into cubes
3 large or 4 small tomatoes, sliced crosswise
dried thyme
pepper

10 eggs
½ cup (120 ml) milk
salt and pepper

1. Preheat the oven to 400°F (200°C).
2. Oil a 10 x 12-inch (25 x 30-cm) baking dish. Add a single layer of zucchini and sprinkle with thyme and pepper.
3. Distribute half of the feta over the zucchini.
4. Add a layer of tomatoes and sprinkle with additional thyme and pepper.
5. Add another layer of zucchini and the remaining feta, and again sprinkle with thyme and pepper.
6. Whisk together the eggs and milk. Add salt and pepper to taste. Pour the egg mixture over the vegetables and feta.
7. Top with a final layer of tomatoes and another sprinkle of thyme and pepper.
8. Bake for 40 to 60 minutes or until the egg mixture is firm.

Serve with a green salad.

Note: If you keep the top layer of tomatoes free of the egg mixture, you allow the tomatoes to acquire the taste of sun-dried tomatoes when baked.

Fennel Casserole with Cream

serves 4

This recipe goes back to my high school years, and I got it from my oldest best friend, Tine Baranowski. The combination of vegetables, cream and nutmeg yields a lovely and very satisfying taste experience.

2 large or 3 small bulbs fennel, cut into bite-size pieces
3 large or 4 small carrots, cut into chunks
2 potatoes, peeled, cut into chunks
salt and pepper
freshly grated nutmeg
3/4 cup (200 ml) heavy cream
a few parsley leaves

1. Preheat the oven to 450°F (250°C).
2. Butter a deep baking dish, around 10 inches (25 cm) in diameter. Place the fennel, carrots and potatoes into the baking dish and sprinkle with salt, pepper and nutmeg to taste. Pour in the cream.
3. Cover with a lid or aluminum foil and bake for 60 minutes or until the vegetables are soft.

Garnish with parsley and serve with cooked whole grains.

Stuffed Pumpkin

serves 6

This festive pumpkin dish is inspired by a creation that my dear friend composer Lisa Karrer brought to the farm. It is a wonderful way of using pumpkins when they are harvested in abundance in the autumn. It always elicits delighted oohs and aahs when brought to the table.

2 cups (480 ml) water
1 cup (240 ml) brown rice, rinsed
1 tablespoon olive oil
2 pinches salt

1 medium onion, chopped
1 pound (500 g) mushrooms, cleaned, cut into slivers
3 tablespoons olive oil
salt and pepper

2/3 cup (160 ml) walnuts, broken into small pieces
1 can (15 ounces or 420 g) corn, drained
1 red bell pepper, cut into small cubes
2 cups (480 ml) grated cheese, divided in half

1 small pumpkin
1 tablespoon olive oil
salt and pepper

1. Preheat the oven to 400°F (200°C).
2. Bring the water to a boil. Add the rice, oil and salt and bring to a second boil, then reduce the heat to its lowest setting and simmer untouched for 45 minutes.
3. Sauté the onions and mushrooms in the oil. Add salt and pepper to taste.
4. When the rice is cooked, combine with the sauté. Stir in the walnuts, corn, bell pepper and 1 cup (240 ml) of the grated cheese.
5. Cut off and discard the top quarter of the pumpkin. Remove the seeds and fibers from the bottom part of the pumpkin and cut its upper edge into a zigzag pattern. Spread the oil inside the pumpkin and sprinkle in salt and pepper to taste.
6. Fill the pumpkin with the rice mixture and sprinkle the remaining grated cheese on top. Cover the top with aluminum foil and bake until the pumpkin meat turns soft, at least 1 hour.

Note: When buying canned corn, always choose a brand that uses no added sugar.

Baked Carrot Sticks

serves 6

Children, too, will love this dish! It's almost as good as french fries. You may want to leave out the rosemary for the kids.

1 pound (500 g) carrots, cut into finger-size sticks
2 tablespoons olive oil
2 teaspoons finely chopped rosemary
salt and pepper

1. Preheat the oven to 425°F (225°C).
2. Place the carrots on a cookie sheet or in a large baking dish.
3. Sprinkle the carrots with the oil and handle each piece until all are evenly coated.
4. Arrange in a single layer and sprinkle with the rosemary.
5. Bake until tender, about 20 minutes.

Sprinkle with salt and pepper to taste and serve hot.

Baked Green Beans

serves 6

This is a surprisingly delicious way of preparing green beans. Don't expect leftovers!

1 pound (500 g) green beans, ends trimmed
2 tablespoons olive oil
salt

1. Preheat the oven to 425°F (225°C).
2. Place the beans on a cookie sheet or into a large baking dish.
3. Sprinkle the beans with the oil and handle each bean until all are evenly coated.
4. Spread the beans evenly and bake until tender and browned, about 30 to 45 minutes. Check after 15 minutes and stir.

Sprinkle with salt to taste and serve hot.

Baked Root Vegetables

serves 6

A colorful display of grounding root vegetables – deeply nourishing and satisfying during the colder time of the year.

2 beets
2 parsnips
2 carrots
2 turnips
(all peeled, cut into bite-size chunks)
2 tablespoons olive oil
fresh or dried thyme
salt and pepper

1. Preheat the oven to 425°F (225°C).
2. Place the vegetables into a large baking dish.
3. Sprinkle the vegetables with the oil and handle each chunk until all are evenly coated.
4. Arrange the chunks in a single layer and sprinkle with thyme to taste.
5. Bake until the vegetables are tender, about 30 to 45 minutes. Check after 15 minutes and stir.

Sprinkle with salt and pepper to taste and serve hot.

Grains

In grains like wheat, rye, oats, barley, rice, millet, corn, spelt and kamut, the kernel is both the seed and the fruit of a domesticated grass. Buckwheat, quinoa and amaranth are often called grains – and I am calling them grains here, because their use in food preparation is similar. However, botanically they are simply seeds, not true grains.

Grains have played a pivotal role in the development of humanity, as they mark the beginning of agriculture and a settled lifestyle. To this day, different grains are staple foods in different cultures and civilizations around the world. In the Americas, it is corn; in Asia, it is rice. In Africa, people eat millet; in the Middle East, bulgur and couscous, both made from wheat. Scotland and Ireland are famous for oats; Russia for buckwheat and kasha, which is roasted buckwheat. Rye, barley, wheat and oats are widespread in Europe.

Grains contain all the macro- and micronutrients needed by the body. They are a wonderful source of complex carbohydrates. They provide us with long-lasting energy and keep our blood sugar balanced, enabling us to concentrate and enjoy stable moods throughout the day. Grains provide protein as well as small amounts of fat. They also deliver a lot of fiber, known to lower cholesterol and keep our elimination regular. They contain vitamins and minerals such as vitamins E and B, iron, calcium and magnesium. Grains are a magnificently well-rounded whole food.

I would like to stress the importance of eating intact whole grains. Grains that have not been processed in any way aside from drying are the most wholesome. When a grain – which is also a seed – remains in its intact, unprocessed form, its inherent life force is preserved until it encounters moisture. Moisture causes it to sprout and give life to a new plant. Therefore, when you cook an intact whole grain, it remains more vibrant and energetically superior to forms of grain that have been cut into pieces, rolled into flakes or ground into flour. No new life can come of these – processed grains have lost their ability to reproduce. Depending upon how long ago they were processed, they have been devoid of life force for days, weeks or months. An intact whole grain is full of vitality until the moment you decide to cook it. Intact whole grains are superior blood sugar balancers as well. I have noticed that when I eat intact whole-grain kasha for breakfast, it keeps me full for a much longer time than when I eat steel-cut oats. And steel-cut oats keep me energized longer than do rolled oats.

For me, there is also something spiritually satisfying about consuming intact grains. They make me feel whole and very much connected to the cycle of life.

Common and Less Common Grains

Wheat is one of the first grains cultivated by humans. It has been eaten throughout Europe, Asia, North Africa and North America. Today it is probably the most widely consumed grain, though unfortunately it is eaten mostly in its highly processed form of white flour. There are three types of wheat: soft, hard and durum. Soft wheat provides the best flour for cake and pastry. Hard wheat has the highest protein and gluten content and is used mostly for bread. Durum is the hardest wheat and is used exclusively for pasta. The intact kernel is called a wheat berry and can be cooked as is. Wheat kernels come whole, cracked as bulgur, rolled, coarsely ground as cream of wheat and finely ground as whole-wheat or white flour. By-products from the milling of white flour are wheat bran, the outer protective layer of the grain, and wheat germ, the part that actually germinates into a plant. Couscous is a ground, steamed then dried wheat product, processed in a similar manner as pasta.

Rye was first cultivated in northeastern Europe and is a staple food in the Baltics, Russia, Belarus and Ukraine. Rye is extremely cold-hardy and is not very demanding when it comes to soil conditions. It is used mostly for bread. The process of making sourdough bread greatly enhances the digestibility and nutrient content of rye. Making a 100 percent rye bread, however, is an art form. It is tricky, as the loaf can easily turn out too hard. Adding some whole-wheat flour will yield a softer bread. Rye kernels come whole, cracked, rolled and ground as flour.

Oats, another cold-climate grain, are a staple food in Ireland, Scotland and England, arriving there about AD 100 from Central Asia and Russia. For steel-cut oats, which were popularized by the Irish and Scotsmen, the oat kernel is cut into two or three pieces. Oats have high protein content and are most widely used as a breakfast food. It is said that oats are a male aphrodisiac as well as an adaptogen – a food that helps the body adapt to new conditions. Oats help to strengthen nerves and reduce addictive cravings. Oat kernels come whole, steel-cut, rolled, flaked and ground as flour.

Barley might be the oldest cultivated grain. It is extremely adaptable – it can grow in frigid highlands as well as desertlike environments. It originated in southwestern Asia around 8,500 BC. Besides its use as a food, barley is known to provide maltose (grain sugar) in beer making. In fact, beer has been called liquid bread. In traditional Chinese medicine, barley is used to strengthen the kidneys, bladder and liver. Barley kernels come whole, pearled (polished), rolled, coarsely ground as grits and finely ground as flour.

Rice is the staple food of Asian countries, feeding roughly half of the world's population. Brown rice has its bran layers intact and is therefore a whole grain. It has the highest content of B vitamins of all the grains. Other kinds of whole-grain rice are red and black rice. Brown rice comes in three different sizes: short-grain, medium-grain and long-grain. Rice grains come whole, refined (white rice), flaked and ground as flour.

Millet, known to most as birdseed, was brought to the Middle East and the Mediterranean countries by the Mongols. Long a staple of northen Africa, China and India, millet has the highest iron content of any grain, and it is the easiest to digest. An exception among the grains, which are generally acid-forming in the body, millet is neutral. Millet should have a mild, nutlike flavor – a bitter taste is a sign of rancidity. Millet seeds come whole, rolled and ground as flour.

Corn, the primary food of Native Americans from north to south, translates in its original languages to "She who sustains us." It has been known for at least eight thousand years. The corn that we are accustomed to eating fresh as a vegetable is very different from field corn and from popping corn, which is dried before it is either ground or popped. Field corn kernels come whole, cracked, very coarsely ground as grits, coarsely ground as polenta, finely ground as cornmeal or corn flour and refined as cornstarch, which is a powder.

Spelt and **kamut**, ancient relatives of wheat, originated in the Middle East. They provide more nutrients and are easier to digest than wheat, and their lower gluten content makes them better choices for those who are allergic to gluten. Their kernels come whole or ground as flour.

Buckwheat is not a true grain and is not related to wheat at all. It is actually the seed of a plant that is related to rhubarb and sorrel. Buckwheat is the most filling and blood sugar stabilizing of all grains. It also has strong warming properties and is therefore a favorite cold-climate food. It originated in Siberia and Manchuria and is popular today in Eastern Europe and northern Asia. It is blood-building and has been used to strengthen the kidneys and bladder. Roasted buckwheat, also called kasha, is more flavorful than the raw form. Buckwheat kernels comes whole, cracked and ground as flour.

Quinoa from the South American Andes was called Mother Grain by the Incas. Although not a true grain, it is also known as a supergrain, as it is an excellent plant source of complete protein and has the highest protein content – 16 percent – of all grains. Quinoa needs to be rinsed well – the plant produces a natural insect repellent called saponin, which has a bitter taste. The germ of quinoa is curled around the periphery. This tiny white curlicue separates in cooking and provides a delightful crispness to contrast the softness of the cooked grain. Quinoa comes whole and ground as flour.

Amaranth, the miracle grain of the Aztecs, was domesticated more than five thousand years ago in Mexico. Not a true grain, it is the tiny seed of an extremely prolific species that can produce up to fifty thousand seeds from a single plant. It is highly nutritious, providing more protein and calcium than milk, along with magnesium, phosphorous and iron. There would be no world hunger or malnutrition if we learned to harness the power of amaranth! Amaranth seeds come whole and ground as flour.

Wheat, rye, and barley contain gluten, a protein that triggers allergic reactions in many people. Oats, for the most part, also contain gluten because they grow on the same fields as the other three gluten-containing grains, and cross-pollination occurs. But some producers do sell oats that are grown in isolation and are therefore gluten-free. For people with gluten allergy, it is best to stay away from wheat, rye, barley and oats (unless it is stated that the oats are gluten-free) and their products and to eat rice, corn, buckwheat, millet, quinoa and amaranth instead. If you suspect that you might be allergic to gluten, stay away from gluten for three weeks and see whether you feel better without it.

Cooking Grains – Simple and Straightforward

Here are basic cooking instructions for all grains:

1. Measure the grains and rinse them in a bowl filled with cold water, then drain.
2. For wheat berries, rye berries, spelt, kamut and brown rice: to enhance digestibility, soak the grains for one to eight hours, then drain.
3. Bring a measured amount of water to a boil, then add rinsed or soaked grains. Add a little bit of oil or butter and a pinch of salt.
4. Bring the grains to a boil, then reduce the heat to its lowest setting. Cover and simmer until all the water is absorbed. Do not stir the grains while they are simmering, as this might make them mushy.

Toward the end of the estimated cooking time, use a knife to carefully pull the grains away from the side of the pot and check whether all the water has been absorbed. If not, continue to simmer. Once the water is absorbed, remove from the heat and let the pot sit covered for another five to ten minutes.

Rinsing the raw grains in a bowl rather than in a sieve under running water allows any debris in the form of chaff to rise to the top and be poured off easily. You also get a better sense of the cleanliness of the grains, as the water is at first cloudy and then becomes clearer as you continue to rinse. Keep rinsing until the water is clear.

Soaking grains for one to eight hours prior to boiling makes them more easily digestible, and I recommend this step for the heavier grains. The process of soaking neutralizes phytic acid, which is located in the outer layer of the grain and can block mineral absorption. When soaking grains, always discard the soaking water and use fresh water for cooking. When grains are soaked, they actually start the germination process, which increases their protein content.

Bringing the water to a boil before adding the grain allows the grain to remain intact. If you pour the grain into cold water and start the cooking process, the texture of the individual grains is lost. This consistency is fine for porridge, but for a side dish you might prefer distinct, separate kernels. Buckwheat in particular should not touch water prior to boiling. Do not even rinse buckwheat.

Energetically, grains are warming and drying. All grains except amaranth, quinoa, buckwheat and millet are acid-forming. To balance the drying and acid-forming properties of grains, I always add a little oil or butter and salt in the cooking process.

For cooking, the relationship between grain and water quantities varies from grain to grain, as does cooking time – see the chart below. Soaking the grains cuts down on cooking time by about half.

Cooked grains keep well in the refrigerator. Because some take considerable time to prepare, it makes sense to cook more than you need for one meal and have some extra for the next day. In the morning you can add extra water or milk when reheating to make porridge from leftover grains. Sprinkle with spices like cinnamon or cardamom, or add a dash of vanilla for flavor. Other delicious additions are nuts, seeds, raisins or other dried fruits. For lunch, turn grains into tasty salads by adding raw or cooked vegetables, scallions, fresh herbs and a dressing made from olive oil and lemon or lime juice (page 114). Cooked grains also make nourishing additions to soups – simply add them at the end of the cooking process (page 176).

Experience different grains for their varied nutritional properties and unique textures and flavors.

Cups of Water and Minutes of Cooking Time for One Cup of Unsoaked Grain

Type of grain	Cups of water	Minutes to cook
INTACT WHOLE GRAINS		
Least cooking time:		
buckwheat or kasha	2	15
quinoa	2	15
millet	3	15
amaranth	2½	20
More cooking time:		
wild rice	2	30
brown rice	2	45
barley	3	45
Most cooking time:		
wheat berries	3	60
spelt	3	60
kamut	3	60
oats	3	60
rye berries	3	90
PROCESSED WHOLE GRAINS		
couscous (ground, steamed, dried wheat)	1	5
bulgur (cracked, steamed, dried wheat)	2	15
polenta (coarsely ground corn)	3	15
steel-cut oats	3	20

RYE

OATS

BARLEY

WILD RICE

MILLET

POLENTA

KASHA

BROWN RICE

RED RICE

SPELT

QUINOA

AMARANTH

Nuts and Seeds

Botanically, nuts are single-seeded fruits with tough, inedible shells. Sweet chestnuts and hazelnuts are true nuts. Most other foods that we call nuts are actually relatives of fruits or they are seeds or legumes. Nuts are a nutritious food source high in protein and fat and rich in calcium, phosphorous, magnesium and potassium. While still in their shells, they stay fresh for a long time. Once shelled, their high oil content makes them prone to rancidity, so it is best to consume them within a week of cracking the shell. Refrigerating shelled nuts will extend their freshness.

Raw nuts are difficult to digest, but roasting or soaking them makes them more easily digestible. Roasting seals the outer layer of the nut, halting oxidation and therefore rancidity. It also intensifies the flavor by crisping and drying out the nut and creating a wonderful aroma. Soaking for several hours or overnight brings to life dormant enzymes that help with digestion. It also neutralizes the action of phytic acid, which otherwise can hamper mineral absorption. Drain and rinse soaked nuts and eat them as is or roast them to enhance the flavor.

Nuts are a great addition to grain and vegetable dishes, salads and desserts. See recipes for Red Rice Salad with Hazelnuts and Dried Cherries (page 114), Wheat Berry Salad with Almonds and Sage (page 120), Russian Kale with Raisins and Roasted Pine Nuts (page 140), Zucchini Walnut Muffins (page 210), Green Salad with Goat Cheese, Cashews and Pears (page 224), Carrot Salad with Pumpkin Seeds (page 228), Alegría (page 256) and Apple Cranberry Hazelnut Crisp (page 264).

Nuts can be made into a delicious milk substitute that is preferable to soy milk (page 39). Soak the nuts overnight, drain and rinse them, then grind them with water in a blender. Strain the liquid through a fine mesh strainer, and the result is a nourishing nut milk.

Nuts and seeds can be made into delicious "butters" – simply 100 percent nuts or seeds ground into a paste. Enjoy nut or seed butters as energizing bread spreads or dips for vegetables.

Oils made from nuts are wonderful for skin care as well as for food. Always look for cold pressed or expeller pressed (a mechanical process that does not create heat) and unrefined oils. With the exception of almond and peanut oils, which are high in monounsaturated fatty acids, never use nut oils for cooking. Instead, use them in dressings and sprinkled over hot food when serving, as most are high in polyunsaturated fatty acids and become rancid when heated. See the chapter on oils (page 41).

Energetically, nuts are very powerful, as they contain the seeds of large trees. Each nut bears the potential of growing into a huge tree, so do not eat too many of them in one sitting!

When eaten in excess, nuts can be challenging to the liver because of their high fat content.

Grain Recipes

Millet with Carrots

serves 4

Millet is one grain that I find a little boring on its own. So I like to dress it up – with carrots, for example.

3 cups (720 ml) water
2 carrots, quartered lengthwise, then sliced crosswise
1 cup millet (240 ml), rinsed
1 tablespoon olive oil
salt and pepper

1. Place the water and carrots into a pot and bring to a boil. Boil for 5 minutes.
2. Add the millet, oil and salt and pepper to taste. Bring to a second boil, then reduce the heat to its lowest setting and simmer, covered and untouched, for 15 minutes or until all the water is absorbed.
3. Remove the pot from the heat and let it sit for another 5 minutes.

Fluff with a fork and serve.

Variation: Prior to serving, gently fold in finely chopped parsley.

Kasha Casserole

serves 8

This is a great-tasting recipe my mother came up with in an attempt to use leftover kasha. It is so delicious that you can, of course, make it from scratch.

4 cups (1 l) water
2 cups (500 ml) kasha
1 tablespoon olive oil
4 pinches salt

5 onions, chopped
2 tablespoons olive oil
4 carrots, cut in half lengthwise, then sliced crosswise
1 medium cabbage (white or red), chopped
salt and pepper

10 eggs
½ cup (120 ml) milk

1. Preheat the oven to 400°F (200°C).
2. Bring the water to a boil. Add the kasha (never add kasha to cold water – it will turn out mushy), the tablespoon of oil and the 4 pinches of salt. Bring to a second boil, then reduce the heat to its lowest setting and simmer, covered and untouched, for 15 minutes or until all the water is absorbed.
3. In a large pot, sauté the onions in the 2 tablespoons of oil for 5 minutes. Add the carrots, cabbage and a little water. Cover and simmer until the vegetables are tender, 5 to 10 minutes.
4. Combine the cabbage mixture with the cooked kasha. Add salt and pepper to taste.
5. Whisk together the eggs and milk. Pour over the kasha mixture and stir.
6. Spread the kasha mixture in an oiled 8 x 12-inch (20 x 30-cm) baking dish.
7. Bake for one hour or until the egg becomes firm.

Serve with sour cream and a tomato salad.

Quinoa Pilaf with Shitake Mushrooms

serves 4 to 6

This is a great blending of sophisticated flavors and textures: quinoa with its light feel and nut-like flavor, onions with their inherent deep sweetness and shitake mushrooms with their savory, earthy tone. Shitake mushrooms have quite a reputation for their medicinal properties. They help detoxify the body and contain antiviral and antitumor substances. Shitakes also support the cardiovascular system.

1 medium onion, chopped
2 cups (480 ml) shitake mushrooms, cut into strips
2 tablespoons olive oil
salt and pepper

2 cups (480 ml) water
1 cup (240 ml) quinoa, rinsed
one handful parsley leaves, chopped fine

1. Sauté the onion and mushrooms in the oil until the liquid from the mushrooms has evaporated. Add salt and pepper to taste.
2. Add the water and bring to a boil. Add the quinoa and bring to a second boil. Reduce the heat to its lowest setting and simmer, covered and untouched, for 15 minutes or until all the water is absorbed.
3. Add the parsley just before serving – fold it in gently, without crushing the quinoa.

Note: Always discard the lower portion of the shitake mushroom stem, as it can be woody and hard. If shitakes are not available, substitute chanterelle, baby portobello, champignon or oyster mushrooms.

Polenta with Roasted Sunflower Seeds

serves 4 to 6

Polenta is a traditional Italian dish with countless variations. This variation evolved over several summers at Polli Talu. The roasted sunflower seeds and golden sautéed onions add richness, and the raisins add sweetness – a combination that is hard to resist.

½ cup (120 ml) raw sunflower seeds
3 cups (720 ml) water
3 pinches salt
1 cup (240 ml) polenta (coarsely ground corn)
1 medium onion, minced
2 tablespoons olive oil
salt and pepper
½ cup (120 ml) raisins

1. Preheat the oven to 425°F (225°C).
2. Spread the sunflower seeds on a cookie sheet and roast until slightly brown, about 5 minutes. Be careful not to burn them – once you smell the aroma, they are done.
3. Bring the water to a boil and add the 3 pinches of salt. Pour the polenta into the water gradually while stirring constantly. When the polenta begins to thicken, reduce the heat to its lowest setting and simmer, covered, for 15 minutes, stirring occasionally.
4. Sauté the onion in the oil until golden. Add salt and pepper to taste.
5. Add the sauté, roasted sunflower seeds and raisins to the polenta and mix well.
6. Pour the polenta mixture into an oiled 8 x 12-inch (20 x 30-cm) baking dish and bake for 20 minutes.

Serve with vegetables and Parsley Dressing (page 217).

Note: Cut any leftover polenta into thick slices and fry the next morning for a delicious breakfast.

Red Rice Salad with Hazelnuts and Dried Cherries

serves 4

Inspired by a salad at the Beacon Natural Market near my home in New York, I came up with this nutty rice salad that goes well with holiday meals in the colder seasons.

Salad:

2 cups (480 ml) water
1 cup (240 ml) red rice, rinsed
2 pinches salt
1 tablespoon olive oil
½ cup (120 ml) raw hazelnuts, cut in half
¾ cup (180 ml) diced celery
½ cup (120 ml) dried cherries

Dressing:

juice of 1 to 2 lemons
4 to 6 tablespoons olive oil
salt and pepper

1. Preheat the oven to 400°F (200°C).
2. Bring the water to a boil and add the rice, salt and oil. Bring to a second boil, then reduce the heat to its lowest setting and simmer, covered and untouched, for 45 minutes.
3. Spread the hazelnuts on a cookie sheet or in a baking dish and roast until you can smell the aroma, about 10 minutes. When the nuts have cooled, remove any loose skin.
4. When the rice is cooked, spread it on a large plate to cool, then transfer to a bowl.
5. Fold in the roasted hazelnuts, celery and cherries.
6. Combine the dressing ingredients in a glass jar. There should be about twice as much lemon juice as oil. Close the lid and shake to mix.
7. Pour the dressing over the rice mixture and stir. Let the salad marinate for ½ to 1 hour.
8. Just before serving, toss gently and adjust seasoning if necessary.

Note: Dried cranberries can be substituted for dried cherries.

Barley Salad

serves 4 to 6

This barley salad is inspired by a recipe from master chef Peter Berley's *The Modern Vegetarian Kitchen.* It is a delight for the eyes as well as the taste buds. We traditionally serve it for lunch on the first day of our weeklong summer retreats. Guests find it so beautiful that nobody wants to be first to disturb the design.

Salad:

6 cups (1½ l) water
⅔ cup (160 ml) barley, rinsed
1 teaspoon salt
1 yellow squash, cut into cubes
1 zucchini, cut into cubes
1 tablespoon olive oil
1 long cucumber, peeled, cut into cubes
1 cup (240 ml) cubed mixed-color bell peppers
1 red onion, chopped fine
2 tablespoons finely chopped scallions
2 tablespoons snipped dill
a few tender arugula leaves or edible flowers

Dressing:

juice of 1 to 2 lemons
4 to 6 tablespoons olive oil
1 teaspoon salt
pepper

1. Bring the water to a boil. Add the barley and salt. Cook over medium heat for 45 minutes or until the barley becomes soft. Pour the cooked barley into a sieve and rinse under cold running water until cool. Place the sieve over a bowl to drain.
2. Sauté the squash and zucchini in the oil for about 4 minutes. Pour the sautéed vegetables into a sieve and rinse under cold running water until cool. Place the sieve over a bowl to drain.
3. In a large bowl, combine the sauté, cooked barley, cucumber, bell pepper, onion, scallion and dill.
4. Combine the dressing ingredients in a glass jar. There should be about twice as much lemon juice as oil. Close the lid and shake to mix.
5. Pour the dressing over the salad and mix well. Let the salad marinate for at least ½ hour.
6. Just before serving, toss gently and adjust lemon juice and seasoning if necessary.
7. Transfer the salad into a bowl small enough for the salad to reach the rim. Turn the bowl upside down onto a serving platter. Carefully remove the bowl and garnish the salad mound with the arugula or with edible flowers like calendula or nasturtium.

Note: Arugula leaves droop quickly, so garnish just before serving.

Quinoa Beet Salad

serves 6

The beets give this dish a most amazing magenta coloring. Bring this to your table and everybody will gasp with delight – guaranteed!

Salad:

2 medium beets, tops removed, whole
2 cups (480 ml) water
1 cup (240 ml) quinoa, rinsed
2 pinches salt
1 bulb fennel, cut into small cubes
1 bunch scallions, chopped
1 handful chopped basil plus a few leaves

Dressing:

juice of 1 to 2 lemons
4 to 6 tablespoons olive oil
salt and pepper

1. Place the whole, unpeeled beets into a pot, add water to cover and boil until soft, about 40 to 60 minutes.
2. In a separate pot, bring the 2 cups (480 ml) of water to a boil and add the quinoa and salt. Bring to a second boil, then reduce the heat to its lowest setting and simmer, covered and untouched, for 15 minutes or until all the water is absorbed. Spread the cooked quinoa on a large plate to cool.
3. When the beets are soft, douse them in cold water until cool, then peel and cut them into small cubes.
4. Combine the cooked quinoa and beets in a bowl and add the fennel, scallions and chopped basil.
5. Combine the dressing ingredients in a glass jar. There should be about twice as much lemon juice as oil. Close the lid and shake to mix.
6. Pour the dressing over the salad and mix well. Let the salad marinate for at least ½ hour.
7. Just before serving, toss gently and adjust lemon juice and seasoning if necessary.

Garnish with basil leaves and serve with a green salad.

Wheat Berry Salad with Sage

serves 6

This festive salad has medieval charm. It provides a beautiful side dish to any winter holiday dinner. It also travels well to your next potluck destination.

Salad:

4 cups (1 l) water
1 cup (240 ml) wheat or spelt berries, soaked overnight in 3 cups water, drained
1 tablespoon olive oil
1 teaspoon salt
½ cup (120 ml) almonds, soaked overnight in 1 cup water, drained
2 carrots, peeled, quartered lengthwise then sliced thin crosswise
½ cup (120 ml) dried apricots, cut into small cubes
5 fresh sage leaves, cut crosswise into thin strips

Dressing:

juice of 1 to 2 limes
2 teaspoons honey
2 tablespoons olive oil
pepper

1. Bring the water to a boil. Add the soaked wheat berries, oil and salt. Bring to a second boil, then reduce the heat to its lowest setting and simmer, covered, for 30 to 45 minutes. Cook only until the wheat berries are soft – remove from the heat before the berries open and lose their shape. Pour them into a sieve and rinse under cold water until cool. Place the sieve over a bowl to drain.
2. Submerge the soaked almonds in boiling water for 5 minutes. Then douse them in cold water. Remove the skins and break them into their halves.
3. Steam the carrots until tender. Rinse them in cold water and drain.
4. Transfer the cooked wheat berries and carrots and the blanched almonds into a large bowl and stir in the apricots and sage.
5. Combine the dressing ingredients in glass jar. There should be about three times as much lime juice as oil. Close the lid and shake to mix.
6. Pour the dressing over the salad and toss. Let the salad marinate for at least 1 hour.
7. Just before serving, toss again and adjust lime juice and seasoning if necessary.

Note: Soaking makes the wheat berries easier to digest and shortens cooking time. This dish keeps well in the refrigerator for three to five days. It tastes even better the next day, when the dried apricots have fully absorbed the dressing. Sage has a very bold flavor, so cut the leaves into very thin strips.

Variation: Substitute celery greens for the sage.

Spaghetti Aglio e Olio à la Polli

serves 6

The traditional Italian spaghetti side dish gets a little twist in our Polli Talu version.

Sauce:

2 medium onions, halved lengthwise then sliced into crescents
3 tablespoons olive oil
6 cloves garlic, sliced
6 scallions, chopped
salt and pepper

Pasta:

1 pound (500 g) whole-grain spaghetti
salt and olive oil

1. Sauté the onions in the oil until slightly golden. Add the garlic and sauté for another 2 minutes, then add the scallions and salt and pepper to taste.
2. Cook the pasta according to the instructions on the package, adding some salt and olive oil to the cooking water. Drain and transfer to a large serving bowl.
3. Pour the sauté over the spaghetti and toss.
4. Just before serving, drizzle a little more olive oil over the dish.

Serve with fish or chicken and vegetables.

Note: The taste of olive oil changes dramatically during the cooking process. Add some more olive oil to your food when serving it to enrich the dish with the lovely aromatic flavor of unheated olive oil.

Pasta with Raw Tomato Sauce

serves 6

A seasonal recipe inspired by my dear friend Lisa Karrer. Make this dish in the summer when there is an abundance of great-tasting local tomatoes – capture their juicy and cooling properties.

Sauce:

10 to 12 medium tomatoes, diced
basil leaves
parsley leaves
cilantro leaves and tender stems
(basil, parsley, cilantro: 1 handful finely chopped of each)
1 bunch chives, snipped
1 handful dill, snipped
1 bunch scallions, chopped fine
½ to ¾ cup (120 to 180 ml) olive oil
salt and pepper

Pasta:

1 pound (500 g) whole-grain pasta, any shape
salt and olive oil

1. Combine the tomatoes and herbs in a large serving bowl. Add a generous amount of olive oil and salt and pepper to taste. Keep at room temperature.
2. Cook the pasta according to the instructions on the package, adding some salt and olive oil to the cooking water. Drain the cooked pasta.

Ladle the sauce over hot pasta on individual plates and serve with a green salad.

Pasta with Mushroom Cream Sauce

serves 6

I just love it when all ingredients come together in harmony, supporting each other to produce a taste experience that is so much richer than the sum total of its components.

Sauce:

1 medium onion, chopped
2 tablespoons olive oil
1 pound (500 g) champignon or baby portobello mushrooms, cut into slivers
salt and pepper
2 cups (480 ml) heavy cream
1 handful finely chopped parsley leaves

Pasta:

1 pound (500 g) whole-grain pasta, any shape
salt and olive oil

1. Sauté the onion in the oil until golden. Add the mushrooms and continue to sauté until all the liquid from the mushrooms has evaporated. Add salt and pepper to taste.
2. Add the cream and boil gently while stirring until the mixture thickens.
3. Just prior to serving, stir in the parsley.
4. Cook the pasta according to the instructions on the package, adding some salt and olive oil to cooking water. Drain the cooked pasta.

Ladle the hot sauce over pasta on individual plates and serve with a green salad.

Pasta with Black Bean Tomato Sauce

serves 6

In this hearty dish, pasta is infused with the Mexican flavor of black beans paired with cilantro. You can substitute cooked dried black beans for the canned beans.

Sauce:

2 medium onions, chopped
4 carrots, sliced into rounds
2 tablespoons olive oil
5 cloves garlic, cut into slivers
16 fresh tomatoes, cut into pieces
(or 6 cups (1½ l) canned crushed tomatoes)
2 cans (15 ounces or 420 g each) black beans, drained and rinsed
2 pinches cayenne pepper
salt and pepper
1 bunch scallions, chopped fine
1 handful chopped cilantro leaves and tender stems

Pasta:

1 pound (500 g) whole-grain pasta, any shape
salt and olive oil

1. In a large pot, sauté the onions and carrots in the oil. When both are tender, add the garlic and sauté a little longer.
2. Add the tomatoes and cook for 20 minutes, stirring occasionally.
3. Add the beans and continue to cook until the beans are thoroughly heated. Add the cayenne pepper and salt and pepper to taste.
4. Cook the pasta according to the instructions on the package, adding some salt and olive oil to the cooking water. Drain the cooked pasta.
5. Just prior to serving, stir the scallions and cilantro into the sauce.

Ladle the sauce over pasta on individual plates and serve hot.

Leafy Greens

Leafy greens add great variety and color to your meals, yet they are one category of whole foods still missing at most tables. Among the very common wild edible leafy green plants are nettle, dandelion greens, lamb's quarters, ramps and sorrel. And among the commonly cultivated vegetables, cabbage can be considered a leafy green. But then there are kale, collard, Swiss chard, mustard greens, spinach, broccoli rabe, bok choy, arugula and watercress. Other leafy greens grow on top of common garden vegetables – for example, beet greens, turnip greens, radish greens, rutabaga greens and the leaves that a broccoli plant produces. These are not only edible, but delicious, too.

Leafy greens are the most nutrition-filled land vegetables. As the green part of the plant, they contain chlorophyll, a pigment they use to capture sunlight and form oxygen. Leaves are, in essence, the lungs of the plant, and consuming them brings energy to our own lungs.

You will feel a burst of energy within minutes of eating greens. If you make them a regular part of your diet, they will uplift your spirits and infuse you with potent sun energy. Green is the color of spring, of renewal, of hope, of the heart chakra – one of the energy centers in the body. No wonder green leafy vegetables have such positive effects on us.

On a nutritional level, leafy greens provide us with an abundance of minerals, vitamins and other valuable substances. They contain iron (the darker the green, the more iron), calcium (Where do cows get the calcium to make milk? From the green grass!), magnesium, potassium, phosphorous, zinc and vitamins A, C, E and K. Leafy greens also deliver fiber, folic acid and, of course, chlorophyll. Chlorophyll nourishes the friendly bacteria in the digestive tract, thus promoting healthy intestinal flora, strengthening immunity and preventing cancer.

Leafy greens have cleansing properties, helping to support liver and kidney function. The bitter-tasting leafy greens, such as watercress, dandelion, arugula and broccoli rabe, are great liver tonics. All leafy greens are excellent blood purifiers, and they improve circulation. They help reduce mucus and clear congestion, especially in the lungs.

Please be aware of two cautions regarding leafy greens:

- Beet greens, Swiss chard and spinach contain oxalic acid, which can leach calcium out of our bones and teeth. Eat these in moderation and combine them with other calcium-rich foods such as legumes, dairy and fish.
- Vitamin K-containing foods such as leafy greens should be eaten sparingly by people who take the blood-thinning medication warfarin (commonly known as Coumadin), which prevents blood clots by blocking the action of vitamin K. Because leafy greens are an abundant source of vitamin K, eating them can undermine the drug's protection against blood clots.

Leafy greens are easy and quick to prepare. The most time-consuming part of preparation is washing the greens. I recommend that you fill your sink with cold water, cut the greens into pieces that suit your recipe and submerge them in the water. With your hands, move the greens about to dislodge any earth or sand particles. If you find a lot of debris at the bottom of your sink, repeat the procedure.

After washing the greens, place them in a colander to drain. It is good to leave a little water on the leaves, as it provides some steaming action if you choose to sauté.

You can steam, boil or sauté greens. Save any cooking liquid to enjoy as a soothing and alkalizing drink. The cooking time for leafy greens is very brief – anywhere from two to five minutes. Always keep a watchful eye – the brightness of the green color will give you a clue as to when they are ready. When the color turns a more vibrant green, that is your signal to check whether they are done. If you cook them for too long, their color changes to olive green and they lose both visual appeal and flavor. Once they turn bright green and are ready, serve them right away, unless you plan to use them in a cold salad – you would rinse them in cold water at that point to stop them from cooking.

When serving greens to my guests, I cut and wash the greens beforehand, but I don't actually cook them until right then and there – while my guests are sitting at the dining table. There is nothing more delicious than freshly cooked greens that were prepared just a minute ago.

When cooking greens, use some form of oil or fat, whether in the cooking process or drizzled over the finished dish, as this will help with the absorption of fat-soluble vitamins A, E and K. Squeezing a little lemon or lime juice or white balsamic vinegar over the dish will help to pull more calcium out of the greens.

Leafy greens are easy to grow, so if you have a garden, give them a try. If you grow root vegetables as well, remember to take advantage of the green part that grows above the earth. But when you harvest the root greens, never remove all of the leaves from a single plant, as the root needs the leaves in order to grow properly. Picking a leaf here and a leaf there will not compromise the root. If you do not own a garden, you can ask a farmer at the market to bring you the green tops of root vegetables or the leaves of broccoli plants. The farmer will happily provide you with these otherwise discarded delicacies.

When buying greens, make sure they are fresh. Do not buy greens that are limp or have turned yellow – you do not want any wilted energy in your body! And try to use them the same day you purchase them or the day after. Unlike other vegetables, greens do not keep well in the refrigerator. So before refrigerating them, I cut off the ends of the stems and place the greens upright in a tall container of water. The stems draw in the water and keep the leaves strong and firm for a day or two.

RAMPS

CURLY KALE

SWISS CHARD

RUSSIAN KALE

LAMB'S QUARTERS

DANDELION GREENS

COLLARD

Leafy Greens Recipes

Sautéed Greens with Garlic
serves 4

This is a simple, very basic recipe you can use with any of your favorite greens.

2 cloves garlic, sliced
1 tablespoon olive oil
1 bunch leafy greens such as kale or collard, stems removed, cut into 1-inch (2-cm) strips
2 pinches salt

1. Sauté the garlic in the oil for 1 minute.
2. Add the greens and sprinkle them with the salt.
3. Stir continuously so that all of the leaves come in contact with the heat.
4. When all of the leaves have turned bright green and are tender, remove from the heat.

Serve with lemon or lime wedges and sprinkle a little juice over the greens prior to eating.

Swiss Chard with Blood Oranges

serves 4

A colorful and tasty delight. Swiss chard can have white, pink, red or yellow stems. These are softer than those on kale or collards, and I often include them in my recipes. If blood oranges are unavailable, a regular orange will do.

2 cups (480 ml) water
2 pinches salt
1 bunch Swiss chard, stems cut into slices, leaves cut crosswise into 1-inch (2-cm) strips
1 blood orange, peeled, separated and cut into chunks
3 tablespoons olive oil
pepper

1. In a large pot, bring the water to a boil. Add the salt and chard and cook covered over high heat, stirring occasionally, until tender, about 5 minutes. Drain and transfer to a serving bowl.
2. Add the orange, oil, and pepper to taste and gently toss.

Serve warm.

Variation: This recipe also works well as a cold salad. After the chard is cooked, remove it from the heat and rinse under cold water. Place the cold chard in a colander and drain. Transfer to a bowl, add the orange, oil and pepper and gently toss.

Russian Kale with Raisins and Roasted Pine Nuts

serves 4

This recipe was inspired by Johnna Albi and Catherine Walthers's *Greens Glorious Greens!*, a wonderful cookbook starring all the great-tasting super-healthful leafy greens. The raisins balance out the slight bitterness of kale.

½ cup (120 ml) pine nuts
2 cups (480 ml) water
1 bunch Russian kale (or any other kale), stalks removed, leaves cut into 1-inch (2-cm) strips
3 cloves garlic, sliced
2 tablespoons olive oil
½ cup (120 ml) raisins
salt

1. Preheat the oven to 400° F (200°C).
2. Spread the pine nuts on a cookie sheet or in a baking dish and roast for 5 minutes or until golden brown. Be careful not to burn the nuts – once you smell the aroma, they are done. Set aside to cool.
3. In a large pot, bring the water to a boil. Add the kale and cook covered over high heat, stirring occasionally, until tender, about 5 minutes. Drain.
4. Sauté the garlic in the oil for 1 minute. Add the raisins and sauté, stirring continuously to prevent burning, until the raisins are glossy and slightly puffed, about 1 minute.
5. Add the cooked kale and a little salt. Mix well and cover for a minute until the kale is heated through.
6. Transfer to a serving bowl and garnish with the roasted pine nuts.

Serve hot.

Lamb's Quarters with Feta

serves 4

Edda, my sister from Canada, inspired this recipe. She introduced me to lamb's quarters while we were spending some time together in upstate New York. Lamb's quarters are one of the most common weeds out there. Because of their wild nature, they are even more nutrient-dense than cultivated greens.

2 cups (480 ml) water
1 pound (500 g) lamb's quarters leaves and tender top portions
1 squeeze lemon juice
3 tablespoons olive oil
9 ounces (250 g) feta, diced
pepper

1. Bring the water to a boil. Add the lamb's quarters and cook covered over high heat, stirring occasionally, until tender, about 5 minutes. Drain.
2. Sprinkle the cooked lamb's quarters with the lemon juice and oil.
3. Add the feta and pepper to taste. Mix carefully and allow the feta to heat through.

Serve warm.

Dandelion Greens in Creamy Sesame Sauce

serves 4

This delicious dish was inspired by Johnna Albi and Catherine Walthers's cookbook, *Greens Glorious Greens!* Use tender, small dandelion greens or any other type of green.

Greens:

2 cups (480 ml) water
1 pinch salt
1 bunch dandelion greens, stems removed, chopped into ½-inch (1-cm) pieces
2 cloves garlic, sliced
2 tablespoons olive oil

Dressing:

3 tablespoons tahini (sesame butter)
5 tablespoons water
1 tablespoon maple syrup
1 tablespoon soy sauce
juice of ½ lemon

1. Bring the water to a boil. Add the salt and dandelion greens and cook covered over high heat, stirring occasionally, until tender, about 3 minutes. Drain.
2. Sauté the garlic in the oil until light golden, 1 to 2 minutes. Stir in the cooked dandelion greens.
3. In a small mixing bowl, combine all dressing ingredients and mix until creamy. At first it will seem as though the tahini is not going to combine with the water and soy sauce. Keep on stirring and it will.
4. Pour the dressing over the cooked greens and stir until the greens are coated.

Serve hot with cooked grains and a root vegetable.

Collard with Marinated Tofu

serves 4

A very earthy dish inspired by a recipe from the Institute for Integrative Nutrition.

7 ounces (200 g) tofu, sliced into ¼-inch (½-cm)-thick pieces
soy sauce
1 large or 2 small onions, halved lengthwise then sliced into crescents
2 portobello mushrooms, sliced
2 tablespoons olive oil
1 pound (500 g) collard, stems removed, leaves cut into 1-inch (2-cm) strips

1. Place the tofu pieces tightly together in a bowl. Add soy sauce to cover and marinate for ½ hour. Reserve the marinade.
2. Sauté the onions and mushrooms in the oil for 10 minutes.
3. Add the collard and a little water. Steam covered, stirring occasionally until the collard is almost tender, about 5 minutes.
4. Add the tofu and cook until the tofu is heated through. Add marinade to taste.

Serve hot over a bed of cooked grains.

Legumes

Legumes – a group that includes beans, peas and lentils, as well as peanuts – are a wonderful and inexpensive source of high-quality nutrition and nourishment. They are packed with fiber, complex carbohydrates, B vitamins, calcium and iron. Legumes are the most complete source of plant-based protein, offering grounding and strengthening energies. The chemical genistein in beans helps to reduce the growth of tumors by preventing blood vessels from attaching to them.

Certain familiar legumes, including green beans, green peas and lima beans, can be harvested when they are immature. In this state, they are considered vegetables. Others, such as lentils and chickpeas, are picked as mature legumes and are generally dried.

In many cultures around the world, legumes and grains are eaten together, and the combination provides the body with a complete set of amino acids. The pairing of rice with beans is a staple in South and Central America, and the grain-and-legume combination appears in Europe as well – as in pea soup, which is traditionally cooked with barley. Kama, an Estonian specialty, is a coarsely ground mixture of peas and grains, eaten with sour milk or yogurt as a light summer meal.

Beans are known to strengthen the kidneys and adrenal glands. Note their similarity in shape to the kidneys! Overtaxed adrenals and kidneys will lead to a decrease in vitality and sexual energy. Beans can help to restore both.

After eating legumes, many people experience digestive difficulties such as gas and intestinal irritability. This is caused by certain complex carbohydrates that do not digest in the small intestines and are later broken down by bacteria in the large intestines, where they release gas. (Similar carbohydrates are found in members of the cabbage family.) If legumes are new to you, start with the smaller ones, such as lentils, mung beans or adzuki beans. Soak and cook your beans for a long enough time and add spices and herbs in the cooking process. Puréeing can also make legumes more easily digestible. Experiment with smaller amounts and gradually build up your tolerance by increasing the size of your portions. However you prepare them, chewing your beans well will facilitate digestion.

Basic Cooking Instructions

Most dried legumes need to be soaked for at least six hours – preferably overnight – to enhance digestibility and to neutralize antinutritional factors that can interfere with mineral absorption. Lentils, split peas and adzuki beans do not need to be soaked.

1. To soak, place rinsed legumes in a pot and add at least four times as much water as there are beans. Soak for at least six hours or overnight – soaking longer than overnight will not hurt legumes.
2. Prior to cooking, discard the soaking water and add fresh water. Bring the legumes to a boil and continue to boil over medium heat. Most legumes (except lentils and chickpeas) produce foam at the beginning of the cooking process. Skim off and discard the foam.
3. Add a piece of seaweed to enhance taste and speed up cooking time. Seaweed plays the same role as the traditional ham bone would: as calcium-rich foods, both help to tenderize legumes.
4. Check the legumes toward the end of the estimated cooking time. They are done when their centers are soft.
5. Wait until the beans are almost cooked before adding salt or soy sauce because salt slows down the cooking process.

Estimated Cooking Time

Cooking time depends on the kind of legume and its degree of dryness, so there is some variation.

Minutes of Cooking Time for Dried Legumes After Soaking	
red lentils	10 to15
French lentils	30 to 45
brown lentils	45 to 60
mung beans	30 to 45
adzuki beans	45 to 60
black beans	60
white beans	60
kidney beans	90
split peas	30
whole peas	60
chickpeas	90

Canned Beans

Although dried legumes that you have soaked and cooked at home are more delicious, canned beans are acceptable as well. If you forgot to soak the beans or don't have the time to cook them, canned versions are just fine. I always have a few cans in my pantry so that I have the option of using a legume recipe right on the spot for a quick, nutritious meal. Here are some tips on using canned beans:

- When purchasing, always check the label for content. Avoid preservatives and added sugar.
- Always drain and rinse the beans.
- Place them into a pot, add a little water and reheat – unless you plan to toss them into a cold salad.
- Add some spices or herbs to enhance flavor. Just a few chopped scallions will turn a plain can of beans into a satisfying dish.

Enjoy legumes as a side dish (pages 154–162) or in a wholesome, filling and yummy soup (pages 166–174).

KIDNEY BEANS

BLACK BEANS

MUNG BEANS

WHITE BEANS

BROAD BEANS

CHICKPEAS

GREEN PEAS

BROWN LENTILS

FRENCH LENTILS

RED LENTILS

Legume Recipes

Black Bean Salad

serves 4

An easy and quick nutritious salad using canned black beans. There is something about cilantro that goes so well with black beans. I know that cilantro is an acquired taste. I must admit that when I was first introduced to it, I did not find it palatable. But over the years I have come to truly love it, and just smelling the fresh herb gives me a nice high.

1 can (15 ounces or 420 g) black beans, drained and rinsed
4 scallions, chopped
1 to 2 cloves garlic, pressed
½ fresh red hot chili pepper, cut into thin rings
1 to 2 tablespoons red balsamic vinegar
1 handful chopped cilantro leaves and tender stems
salt and pepper

1. Combine the beans, scallions, garlic, chili pepper, vinegar and cilantro in a serving bowl.
2. Add salt and pepper to taste and garnish with a sprig of cilantro.

Serve along with other salads in a buffet setting or for lunch with a green salad.

Curried Red Lentils

serves 6

Very basic and quick. The beauty of using lentils, especially the tiny red ones, is that they do not require soaking and can be prepared on the spur of the moment. These lentils cook especially quickly. Red lentils always lose their structure, no matter how carefully you time the cooking. Unfortunately, they also lose their bright orange color and turn yellow. But they are no less tasty!

2 medium onions, chopped
1 teaspoon curry powder
2 tablespoons olive oil
3 cups (720 ml) water
1 cup (240 ml) red lentils, rinsed
salt and pepper
1 handful finely chopped parsley

1. Sauté the onions and curry in the oil until the onions turn golden, about 7 minutes.
2. Add the water and lentils. Cook over medium heat for 10 minutes or until the lentils are soft. Add salt and pepper to taste.
3. Just before serving, stir in the parsley.

Serve hot with cooked brown rice and vegetables.

Note: Sautéing the curry in olive oil is an Indian technique for bringing out the flavor of the spice mixture – it will be more integrated and not seem "raw."

French Lentils with Balsamic Vinegar

serves 6

A very easy and tasty lentil dish. The combination of the bay leaf and balsamic vinegar brings out the lentil flavor. Although French lentils are tiny, they still need at least thirty minutes of cooking time.

- 3 cups (720 ml) water
- 1 cup (240 ml) French lentils, rinsed
- 1 or 2 bay leaves
- 1 to 2 tablespoons red balsamic vinegar
- salt and pepper

1. Place the water, lentils and bay leaf into a pot and bring to a boil. Reduce the heat to its lowest setting and simmer until the lentils are soft, about 30 minutes. Check occasionally to ensure that there is enough water for cooking – add a little more if needed.
2. When the lentils are soft, stir in the vinegar and add salt and pepper to taste.

Serve hot with a cooked grain, such as quinoa, and a leafy green.

Chilean Bean Stew with Corn

serves 6

This lovely dish is inspired by a recipe from *Moosewood Restaurant New Classics* by the Moosewood Collective. Feel free to use canned kidney beans and corn. The flavors of kidney beans, corn and basil mingle beautifully.

- 2 cups (480 ml) chopped onions
- 2 tablespoons olive oil
- 1½ teaspoons salt
- ½ teaspoon pepper
- 1 pinch cayenne pepper
- 1 cup (240 ml) water
- 4 cloves garlic, pressed
- 3 medium zucchinis, cut into cubes
- 3 cups (720 ml) corn, frozen or canned
- 3 cups (720 ml) canned kidney beans
- 1 handful chopped basil

1. In a large pot, sauté the onions in the oil until golden. Add the salt, pepper and cayenne pepper and sauté for another 2 minutes.
2. Add the water, garlic and zucchini and cook over medium heat for 5 minutes.
3. Add 2 cups of the corn, the kidney beans and the basil. Cover and cook over low heat for 5 minutes.
4. Remove 1 cup of liquid from the pot. Combine with the remaining cup of corn and puree in a blender or food processor.
5. Stir the puree into the stew and reheat.

Serve with brown rice, quinoa or freshly baked Corn Bread (page 200) and a green salad.

Note: When buying canned foods – particularly canned corn – choose a brand without added sugar.

Chickpeas with Sweet Potatoes

serves 4

I love the shape of chickpeas, also called garbanzo beans. They don't fall apart while cooking – they keep their interesting chickpea shape.

- 1 medium sweet potato, peeled, quartered lengthwise then cut into 1/4-inch (1/2-cm) slices
- 1 medium onion, chopped
- 1 teaspoon ground cumin
- 3 tablespoons olive oil
- 1 can (15 ounces or 420 g) chickpeas, rinsed and drained
- salt and pepper
- 1 handful finely chopped parsley
- juice of 1/2 or 1 lemon
- 2 cloves garlic, pressed

1. Boil or steam the sweet potato until tender, about 10 minutes. Drain and reserve the cooking liquid.
2. In a separate pot, sauté the onion and cumin in the oil until the onion turns golden, about 5 minutes. Add the chickpeas, the cooked sweet potato and a little of the reserved cooking liquid to reheat. Add salt and pepper to taste.
3. Add the parsley, lemon juice and garlic. Toss and transfer to serving bowl. Sprinkle with additional olive oil before serving.

Serve with a cooked grain like brown rice, millet or quinoa and a leafy green.

Note: I add the garlic at the end of the cooking process to intensify the kick it adds to the dish. If you prefer less intensity, add the garlic to the sauté along with the chickpeas.

White Bean Soup

serves 8

The nice thing about this soup is that the broth stays clear. It's a lighter kind of bean soup, perfect for a spring or summer day.

1½ cups (300 g) dried white beans, soaked overnight, drained and rinsed
8 cups (2 l) water
3 bay laves
1 onion, chopped
4 carrots, halved lengthwise, then sliced crosswise
2 tablespoons olive oil
4 to 5 tomatoes, cut into thin wedges
1 leek, cut into small pieces
salt and pepper
1 bunch scallions, cut diagonally

1. Place the beans and water into a pot and bring to a boil. Skim off and discard any foam that forms. Add the bay leaves and cook over medium heat until the beans begin to soften, about 1 hour.
2. Sauté the onion and carrots in the oil until the onion turns golden.
3. Once the beans are tender, add the sauté and the tomatoes and cook for 5 minutes.
4. Add the leeks and cook for another 3 minutes. Add salt and pepper to taste.
5. Just before serving, stir in the scallions.

Note: Salt slows down the cooking process, so always add salt at the end of the cooking time. In recipes that call for onions and vegetables to be sautéed and then added to a soup or other dish, make sure to transfer every bit of the good flavor from the sauté pan after you have removed the onion mixture – add a little water to the pan, reheat, stir, and pour this sauté residue into your dish.

Kidney Bean Soup

serves 6

This bean soup, one of our favorites at the farm, has a rich flavor that is enhanced by a little sweetness from the corn and a little tartness from the tomatoes.

2½ cups (500 g) dried kidney beans, soaked overnight, drained and rinsed
8 cups (2 l) water
1 bay leaf
1 onion, chopped
2 large carrots, halved lengthwise, then sliced crosswise
3 tablespoons olive oil
4 to 5 tomatoes, cut into chunks
2 red bell peppers, cut into small pieces
1 can (15 ounces or 420 g) corn, rinsed
1 leek, cut into small pieces
salt and pepper

1. Place the beans and water into a pot and bring to a boil. Skim off and discard any foam that forms. Add the bay leaf and cook over medium heat until the beans begin to soften, about 1 hour.
2. Sauté the onion and carrots in the oil until the onion turns golden.
3. Once the beans are tender, add the sauté and the tomatoes and cook for 10 minutes.
4. Add the bell pepper, corn and leek and cook for another 3 minutes. Add salt and pepper to taste.

Serve topped with sour cream.

Pea Soup with Cardamom

serves 6

Inspired by a soup my dear friend Lisa Karrer used to make, this further-developed version of pea soup is a combination of Indian (ginger and cardamom) and Estonian (barley) flavors. The cardamom suits the pea soup surprisingly well. See for yourself!

2½ cups (500 g) dried yellow peas, half whole, half split
8 cups (2 l) water
1 cup (240 ml) barley
2 onions, chopped
3 carrots, halved lengthwise, then sliced crosswise
1 tablespoon peeled and finely chopped fresh ginger
2 teaspoons ground cardamom
2 tablespoons olive oil
1 large or 2 small leeks, cut into small pieces
salt and pepper

1. Place the peas and water into a pot and bring to a boil. Skim off and discard any foam that forms. Add the barley and cook over medium heat for 1½ hours, stirring occasionally.
2. Sauté the onions, carrots, ginger and cardamom in the oil for 5 minutes.
3. When the peas start to become tender, add the sauté and cook for another 10 minutes.
4. Add the leeks and cook for another 3 minutes. Add salt and pepper to taste.

Serve with dark rye bread and butter.

Lentil Soup with Tomatoes

serves 4 to 6

This is the best lentil soup ever! It tastes even better the next day. Inspired by a recipe from the Institute for Integrative Nutrition.

1½ cups (360 ml) brown lentils, rinsed
4 cups (1 l) water
1 bay leaf
1 onion, chopped
2 carrots, halved lengthwise, then sliced crosswise
2 stalks celery, sliced
1 teaspoon ground cumin
3 tablespoons olive oil
3 cups (720 ml) chopped fresh tomatoes
3 cloves garlic, chopped
1 tablespoon dried thyme
salt

1. Place the lentils, water and bay leaf into a pot. Bring to a boil and cook for 1 hour over medium heat. Add more water if needed.
2. Sauté the onion, carrots, celery and cumin in the oil until the onion turns golden, 5 to 10 minutes.
3. When the lentils are almost soft, add the sauté, tomatoes, garlic and thyme and cook for another 20 minutes. Add salt to taste.

Note: Crushed canned tomatoes can be substituted for the fresh tomatoes.

Black Bean Soup

serves 6

This is the first bean soup I ever made. I had eaten bean, pea or lentil soups before, but I had never actually cooked one myself. It seemed to be a big deal to soak the beans and then cook them. But one day I got inspired and decided to give it a try. I planned it and soaked the beans overnight for a soup to be cooked on a Saturday. I made a big pot of it, which provided me with nutritious food for several days. And that was the beginning of my love affair with homemade bean soups. Now I make one every week. They are so rich and satiating that a bowl of bean soup can serve as dinner.

2½ cups (500 g) dried black beans, soaked overnight, drained and rinsed
8 cups (2 l) water
1 onion, chopped
3 carrots, halved lengthwise, then sliced crosswise
2 tablespoons olive oil
3 leeks, cut into small pieces
salt and pepper

1. Place the beans and water into a pot and bring to a boil. Skim off and discard any foam that forms. Cook over medium heat for 1 hour.
2. Sauté the onion and carrots in the oil for about 10 minutes.
3. When the beans start to become tender, add the sauté and cook for another 10 minutes.
4. Add the leeks and cook for another 3 minutes. Add salt and pepper to taste

Serve garnished with fresh cilantro leaves and topped with sour cream.

Vegetable Soup with Kasha

serves 6

This soup is a vitamin and mineral potion – great in the spring. Kasha gives the soup a little more body and protein. It is a great way to utilize any leftover cooked kasha, but you can substitute any other cooked grain, like brown rice or quinoa.

1 onion, chopped
2 tablespoons olive oil
6 cups (1½ l) boiling water
3 carrots, halved lengthwise, then sliced crosswise
1 small green cabbage, cut into chunks
1 lovage leaf, chopped
1 cup cooked kasha
salt and pepper

nettles (leaves and tender top portions, prior to bloom)
dandelion greens (young ones)
lamb's quarters (leaves and tender top portions)
dill
parsley
scallions
— chopped, 1 handful each

1. In a large pot, sauté the onion in the oil until golden, about 5 minutes.
2. Add the water and carrots and bring to a boil. Cook for 10 minutes.
3. Add the cabbage and lovage. Cook for another 10 minutes.
4. When the vegetables are soft, add the kasha and reheat. Add salt and pepper to taste.
5. Just before serving, stir in the nettles, dandelion greens, lamb's quarters, dill, parsley and scallions.

Serve with dark rye bread and butter.

Note: When a recipe calls for a large amount of boiled water, I save time by boiling the water in a separate vessel. To gather the greens, I usually weed my garden beds in front of the house. If you do not have access to a garden or wild greens, substitute greens like celery leaves or spinach and herbs like chives.

Tomato Soup

serves 6

An intensely delicious soup made without water! Try this recipe at the height of the tomato season. This soup takes some time and effort, but the result is well worth it.

20 medium tomatoes, cut into quarters
2 onions, chopped
2 tablespoons olive oil
3 carrots, halved lengthwise, then sliced crosswise
3 stalks celery, sliced
5 cloves garlic, sliced
1 handful chopped basil
salt and pepper

1. Place the tomatoes into a pot (without water) and bring to a boil. Cook for 1 hour. Stir occasionally, making sure the tomatoes do not burn.
2. Sauté the onions in the oil until golden, about 5 minutes. Add the carrots and celery and sauté for another 10 minutes.
3. Place a sieve over a separate pot and pour in the cooked tomatoes. Work the tomatoes through, using a spoon to push through the juices and meat until only the skins, seeds and tough core parts remain in the sieve.
4. Add the sauté and the garlic to the cooked tomatoes and bring to a boil. Cook for another 5 minutes.
5. Add the basil and salt and pepper to taste.

Serve topped with sour cream and garnish with basil leaves.

Potato Zucchini Soup

serves 8

One of our favorite summer soups at the farm. Simple ingredients and lots of fresh herbs make this creation a winner. The recipe is inspired by a soup that my friend Lisa Karrer made for us at Kütiorg many summers ago.

1 onion, chopped
2 tablespoons olive oil
2 cloves garlic, chopped
6 cups (1½ l) boiling water
1 pound (500 g) potatoes, peeled and cut into chunks
2 zucchinis, ends removed, cut into chunks
salt and pepper

snipped chives
snipped dill
chopped scallions
| 1 handful each

1. In a large pot, sauté the onion in the oil until golden, about 5 minutes. Add the garlic and sauté for another few minutes.
2. Add the water and potatoes and bring to a boil. Cook for 10 minutes.
3. Add the zucchini and bring to a second boil. Cook for 5 minutes, stirring occasionally. Add salt and pepper to taste.
4. Just before serving, stir in the chives, dill and scallions.

Serve with dark rye bread and butter.

Note: In most cases, I add fresh herbs just prior to serving. This allows them to provide a more lively taste experience. If you add them during the cooking process, their flavors infuse the entire soup but do not come to the forefront as much.

Sweet Potato Tomato Soup

serves 8

This soup came about one day when I opened my refrigerator to see what was in there and tried to figure out what I could possibly make from the ingredients I found. It turned out so wonderful that I wrote down the recipe, and it has since become a Polli Talu classic.

- 1 onion, minced
- 2 tablespoons olive oil
- 1 piece fresh ginger, about 2 inches (5 cm) long, peeled and cut into slivers
- 3 cloves garlic, chopped
- 8 cups (2 l) boiling water
- 5 tomatoes, peeled (optional) and chopped
- 2 white potatoes, cut into cubes
- 2 carrots, cut into ½-inch (1-cm) pieces
- 2 sweet potatoes, cut into cubes
- salt and pepper
- ½ bunch scallions, chopped

1. In a large pot, sauté the onion in the oil until golden, about 5 minutes. Add the ginger and then the garlic and sauté for another few minutes.
2. When the garlic turns golden, add the water and tomatoes. Bring to a boil.
3. Add the white potatoes, then the carrots, then the sweet potatoes. Cook until the potatoes and carrots are soft, stirring occasionally. Add salt and pepper to taste.
4. Just before serving, stir in the scallions.

Note: To peel tomatoes, submerge them whole into boiling water for a couple of seconds. Remove them from the water and peel. If your tomatoes do not have a strong flavor and the broth ends up without the desired hint of tartness, add a squeeze of lemon juice.

Mushroom Barley Soup

serves 6

A classic American soup. I tried it a few times when I first came to New York and found it to be the most boring of soups, and I never tried it again. But 27 years later, my client Rachel gave me a taste of her homemade mushroom barley soup. To my surprise, it was totally delicious. I was blown away and begged her to give me the recipe. What makes this version so delicious is the use of butter, soy sauce and sherry. I include carrots as well.

½ cup (120 ml) barley, rinsed
6 cups (1½ l) water
2 onions, chopped
2 cloves garlic, minced
3 tablespoons butter
1 pound (500 g) mushrooms, sliced
1 teaspoon salt
6 tablespoons soy sauce
½ cup (120 ml) medium dry sherry
2 carrots, halved lengthwise, then sliced crosswise
pepper

1. In a large pot, cook the barley in 2 cups (500 ml) of the water until tender, about 1 hour.
2. Sauté the onions and garlic in the butter. When they soften, add the mushrooms and the salt. Continue to sauté until the mushrooms are tender.
3. Stir the sauté into the cooked barley, then add the remaining 4 cups (1 l) water, soy sauce, sherry and carrots. Bring to a boil and simmer, covered, for 20 minutes.
4. Adjust taste by adding more soy sauce or sherry if necessary. Add pepper to taste.

Cold Cucumber Soup

serves 4 to 6

A wonderful cooling and cleansing summer soup inspired by a recipe from the *Yoga Journal* website.

Soup:

2 pounds (1 kg) cucumbers, peeled, large seeds discarded
1 cup (240 ml) plain yogurt
1 handful coarsely chopped herbs (like basil, dill, parsley and cilantro)
½ teaspoon salt
zest and juice of ½ lemon
pepper

Garnish:

1 lovage leaf, cut into very thin strips
zest and juice of ½ lemon
1 tablespoon olive oil
2 pinches salt

scallions
dill
basil
cilantro
(1 tablespoon finely chopped each)

1. Finely chop enough cucumbers to make 1 cup (240 ml) and set aside.
2. Coarsely chop the rest of the cucumbers and place into a blender or food processor. Add the plain yogurt, coarsely chopped herbs, salt, lemon zest and juice and pepper to taste. Puree the mixture and refrigerate.
3. Combine the finely chopped cucumber with the garnish ingredients.
4. Before serving, taste the soup and add a little salt or lemon juice if necessary.

Pour into bowls and top with the garnish.

Carrot Ginger Soup

serves 4 to 6

This soup is absolutely divine. When we serve it at Polli Talu, many guests lick their plates. It is the Zen version of a recipe that I once found on the website of the Institute for Integrative Nutrition.

1 onion, sliced
2 tablespoons olive oil
3 cloves garlic, chopped
1 piece fresh ginger, about 2 inches (5 cm) long, sliced
8 carrots, sliced into rounds
1 medium sweet potato, peeled and sliced thin
4 cups (1 l) boiling water
½ cup (120 ml) orange juice
salt and pepper
2 scallions, chopped, or some parsley leaves

1. In a large pot, sauté the onion in the oil for 7 to 10 minutes.
2. Add the garlic and ginger. Sauté for another 3 minutes.
3. Add the carrots, sweet potato and water. Bring to a boil and cook over medium heat until the carrots are tender, about 15 minutes.
4. Pour the mixture into a blender or food processor and puree until smooth, adding more water if necessary.
5. Return the puree to the pot. Stir in the orange juice and salt and pepper to taste. Bring to a boil.

Pour into soup plates and garnish with chopped scallions or parsley leaves.

Note: The skin of ginger is edible. Because the soup is pureed, there is no need to peel the ginger in this recipe. You can substitute a white potato for the sweet potato.

Cauliflower Leek Soup

serves 4 to 6

A very light summer soup that brings out the subtle flavor of cauliflower, supported with a little sweetness from the leeks. Cauliflower lends itself to pureeing – it takes on a lovely creamy texture.

1 medium cauliflower, cut into florets
2 leeks, cut into small pieces
1 teaspoon freshly grated nutmeg
salt and pepper

1. Place the cauliflower florets into a pot and add enough water to cover. Bring to a boil and cook for 5 minutes.
2. Add the leeks and cook until the leeks are soft but still bright green, about 3 minutes.
3. Pour the mixture into a blender or food processor and puree until smooth.
4. Return the puree to the pot and bring to a boil. Add the nutmeg and salt and pepper to taste.

Pour into soup plates and garnish with a swirl of pumpkinseed oil or brown butter, to which a little salt has been added.

Note: To make brown butter, place 1 to 2 tablespoons of butter in a small pot and cook over medium heat, stirring continuously, until the butter turns light brown.

Kabocha Apricot Soup

serves 6

What could be a better treat than a squash puree soup on a chilly autumn day? Although the original recipe calls for kabocha squash, any winter squash or pumpkin can be used. The dried apricots add a little twist of sweet and tart and a hint of sophistication.

1 kabocha squash, about 2 pounds (1 kg), cut into quarters, seeds and fibrous parts removed
4 cups (1 l) water
1 onion, cut into wedges
12 dried apricots, cut into halves
1 piece fresh ginger, about 2 inches (5 cm) long, sliced
1 tablespoon butter
salt and pepper
2 tablespoons chopped parsley

1. Place the squash in a steamer basket inserted into a large pot. Add 3 cups (750 ml) of the water and steam for 20 minutes. Reserve the cooking water. Place the cooked squash onto a plate to cool. Use a spoon to scrape the meat from the peel.
2. Boil the onion, apricots and ginger in the remaining 1 cup (250 ml) of water for 10 minutes.
3. Combine the squash with the onion mixture. In batches, pour into a blender or food processor and puree, adding some of the reserved squash cooking water for a smooth blend.
4. Return the puree to the pot. Add the butter and bring to a boil. Add more cooking water if the soup is very thick. Add salt and pepper to taste

Pour into soup plates and garnish with chopped parsley.

Pumpkin Apple Soup

serves 6 to 8

This soup is soft as silk. It is inspired by a recipe I found on the *Yoga Journal* website.

3 pounds (1½ kg) pumpkin, seeds and fibrous parts removed, cut into large chunks
4 cups (1 l) water
3 leeks (white and tender green parts), cut into small pieces
3 stalks celery, sliced
2 tablespoons olive oil
3 medium apples, seeds and hearts removed, cut into chunks
1 cup (240 ml) apple cider or juice
1 piece fresh ginger, about ¾ inch (2 cm) long, chopped
½ teaspoon ground cumin
½ teaspoon freshly grated nutmeg
salt and pepper
8 chives, cut into 2-inch (5-cm)-long pieces

1. Place the pumpkin in a steamer basket inserted into a large pot. Add 2 cups (500 ml) of the water and steam for 20 minutes. Reserve the cooking water. Place the cooked pumpkin onto a plate to cool. Use a spoon to scrape the meat from the peel.
2. Sauté the leeks and celery in the oil for 5 minutes. Add the apples, cider, ginger, cumin, nutmeg and the remaining 2 cups (500 ml) of water and bring to a boil. Reduce the heat to its lowest setting and simmer for 10 minutes.
3. In batches, pour the mixture into a blender or food processor and puree, using all of the reserved cooking water for a smooth blend.
4. Return the soup to the pot and reheat. Add salt and pepper to taste.

Pour into soup plates and garnish with crisscrossed pieces of chive.

Karask – Traditional Estonian Barley Bread

serves 8

This is an Estonian folk recipe that I adjusted to include only whole foods and natural sweeteners. The barley flour gives it a distinct, sweet taste.

- 4½ ounces (125 g) farmer cheese
- 1 cup (240 ml) kefir or yogurt
- 1 egg
- 1 teaspoon salt
- 1 teaspoon honey
- 2 tablespoons butter, melted
- 1 cup (240 ml) barley flour
- ½ cup (120 ml) whole-wheat flour
- ½ tablespoon baking soda

1. Preheat the oven to 400°F (200°C).
2. Line a rectangular baking pan (5 x 10 inches or 12 x 25 cm) with parchment paper.
3. Combine the farmer cheese, kefir, egg, salt and honey in a bowl and mix until smooth.
4. Stir in the melted butter.
5. Combine the flours with the baking soda and add to the batter. Mix well.
6. Pour the batter into the pan and bake for 30 to 40 minutes. To check whether the bread is ready, insert a wooden toothpick into the center. When the toothpick comes out dry, the bread is done.

Serve with butter or Onion Butter (page 220).

Corn Bread

serves 8

An American staple. This simple recipe was inspired by *Moosewood Restaurant New Classics* by the Moosewood Collective. Sweetened with maple syrup, it is almost like a cake.

- 1 cup (240 ml) polenta (coarsely ground corn)
- 1 cup (240 ml) whole-wheat flour
- 2 teaspoons baking powder
- 1/2 teaspoon baking soda
- 1/2 teaspoon salt
- 2 eggs
- 1/4 cup (60 ml) olive oil
- 1/4 to 1/3 cup (60 to 80 ml) maple syrup
- 1 cup (240 ml) yogurt, kefir or sour milk

1. Preheat the oven to 425°F (225°C).
2. Line a rectangular baking pan (5 x 10 inches or 12 x 25 cm) with parchment paper.
3. Mix all of the dry ingredients in one bowl.
4. Mix all of the wet ingredients in another bowl.
5. Pour the wet mixture into the dry mixture and stir.
6. Pour the batter into the pan and bake for 20 to 25 minutes. To check whether the bread is ready, insert a wooden toothpick into the center. When the toothpick comes out dry, the bread is done.

Serve with butter.

Variation: The batter also lends itself to making individual corn muffins. Line a muffin tin with paper muffin cups and fill each cup halfway. Bake for 15 minutes.

Rice Oat Corn Bread

serves 8

This lovely bread is from the repertoire of *Angelica's Kitchen*, a vegan restaurant in New York City. It is baked without any flour and contains all the goodness and richness of the whole grains brown rice, corn and oats.

2½ cups (600 ml) water
1 cup (240 ml) brown rice, rinsed
1 teaspoon salt
1⅓ cups (320 ml) rolled oats
1⅓ cups (320 ml) polenta (coarsely ground corn)
1 teaspoon salt
3 cups (720 ml) apple cider or juice
¼ cup (60 ml) almond oil or olive oil

1. Bring the water to a boil. Add the rice and the salt. Bring to a second boil, then reduce the heat to its lowest setting and simmer, covered, for 40 minutes.
2. Preheat the oven to 400°F (200°C).
3. Line a rectangular baking pan (5 x 10 inches or 12 x 25 cm) with parchment paper.
4. Combine the oats, polenta, salt, cider and oil in a large bowl. Add the cooked rice and mix well.
5. Pour the batter into the pan and bake for 75 minutes. To check whether the bread is ready, insert a wooden toothpick into center. When the toothpick comes out dry, the bread is done.

Allow the bread to cool before serving. Cut into thick slices and serve with tahini (sesame butter) and honey.

Leek Quiche

serves 4 to 6

I have always had a reverence for quiche. But I thought it was one of those delicate and complicated French things – until Lise Lotte Urfe from Denmark came to visit the farm and treated us to this tasty example. I was pleasantly surprised by how simple a quiche is to make. Of course, I asked her for the recipe, and I just substituted whole-wheat flour for white flour. It is the combination of leeks, feta and dill that makes this quiche spectacular. Now we serve it frequently – everybody loves it and asks for the recipe.

Crust:

1¼ sticks (150 g) butter

1 cup plus 2 tablespoons (150 g) whole-wheat flour

½ teaspoon baking powder

2 pinches salt

a little cold water

Filling:

1 medium onion, chopped

2 tablespoons olive oil

2 leeks, white and tender green parts, cut into ½-inch (1-cm) pieces

6 eggs

¼ cup (60 ml) heavy cream

1 handful snipped dill

salt and pepper

9 ounces (250 g) feta cheese, cut into cubes

1. Combine the crust ingredients, adding just enough water to form a kneadable dough. Form into a ball. Wrap with plastic wrap and refrigerate for 1 hour.
2. Preheat the oven to 400°F (200°C).
3. Spread the dough in a round quiche pan (10 inches or 25 cm) so that the bottom is covered and the sides are turned up. Prick the dough with a fork and bake until slightly browned, 10 to 15 minutes.
4. Sauté the onion in the oil for 5 minutes. Add the leeks and sauté for another 5 minutes. Let the mixture cool.
5. Whisk together the eggs, cream, dill and salt and pepper to taste.
6. Spread the onion mixture over the baked crust. Pour in the egg mixture.
7. Distribute the feta evenly over the quiche.
8. Reduce the oven temperature to 350°F (175°C) and bake until the egg mixture is firm, 30 to 40 minutes.

Serve warm with a green salad.

Note: You can substitute any vegetable for the leeks. Quiches are a great way to use leftover vegetables! Also try adding other fresh herbs like basil or parsley.

Chanterelle Quiche

serves 4 to 6

A quiche variation with chanterelles – a bit on the wild side. Feel free to use another kind of mushroom or an herb other than parsley.

Crust:

1¼ sticks (150 g) butter

1 cup plus 2 tablespoons (150 g) whole-wheat flour

½ teaspoon baking powder

2 pinches salt

a little cold water

Filling:

1 medium onion, chopped

½ pound (200 g) chanterelles, cut into small pieces

3 tablespoons olive oil

2 carrots, halved lengthwise then sliced crosswise

6 eggs

¼ cup (60 ml) heavy cream

1 handful finely chopped parsley leaves

salt and pepper

1 bunch scallions, chopped

1. Combine the crust ingredients, adding just enough water to form a kneadable dough. Form into a ball. Wrap with plastic wrap and refrigerate for 1 hour.
2. Preheat the oven to 400°F (200°C).
3. Spread the dough in a round quiche pan (10 inches or 25 cm) so that the bottom is covered and the sides are turned up. Prick the dough with a fork and bake until slightly browned, 10 to 15 minutes.
4. Sauté the onion and chanterelles in the oil until the liquid from the mushrooms has evaporated. Add the carrots and sauté for another 5 minutes.
5. Whisk together the eggs, cream and parsley. Add salt and pepper to taste.
6. Sprinkle the scallions over the baked crust, then spread on the mushroom mixture.
7. Pour in the egg mixture.
8. Reduce the oven temperature to 350°F (175°C) and bake until the egg mixture is firm, 30 to 40 minutes.

Serve warm with a green salad.

Vegetable Frittata

serves 4

A frittata is an Italian-style omelet that I like to bake in the oven. It is a tasty opportunity to use up any leftover vegetables. You can include carrots, sweet potatoes, broccoli or any other vegetable.

1 onion, chopped
1 tablespoon olive oil
6 eggs
6 tablespoons water
salt and pepper
1 cup (240 ml) steamed vegetables, cut into small pieces
1 cup (240 ml) boiled potatoes, diced
1 cup (240 ml) halved cherry tomatoes
4 scallions, chopped

1. Preheat the oven to 425°F (225°C).
2. Sauté the onion in the oil until golden, about 5 minutes.
3. Whisk together the eggs and the water. Add salt and pepper to taste.
4. Oil a cast iron pan (10 inches or 25 cm) suitable for baking (no wooden handle!).
5. Pour the egg mixture into the pan.
6. Distribute the vegetable mixture into the egg mixture. Place the pan in the oven and bake for 30 minutes.

Serve with sautéed greens and rye bread.

Variation: Before baking, add some chopped herbs like parsley and basil.

Zucchini Walnut Muffins

yields 12 muffins

An all-time favorite, these muffins are like cake! I got the original recipe from Jolanta Bazyte, a fellow alumna from the Institute for Integrative Nutrition. I had called out for help prior to a cooking class, and she came to the rescue by providing a lovely recipe.

1½ cups (360 ml) whole-wheat flour
2 teaspoons baking powder
½ teaspoon cinnamon
1 pinch salt
2 eggs
⅓ cup (80 ml) olive oil
⅓ cup (80 ml) maple syrup
1 teaspoon vanilla extract
1 small zucchini, grated
½ cup (120 ml) raisins
½ cup (120 ml) walnuts, broken into small pieces

1. Preheat the oven to 400°F (200°C).
2. Butter a pan for 12 standard-size muffins.
3. Combine the flour, baking powder, cinnamon and salt.
4. In a separate bowl, whisk the eggs. Stir in the oil, maple syrup, vanilla and zucchini.
5. Add the flour mixture to the zucchini mixture and stir until evenly moistened.
6. Stir in the raisins and walnuts.
7. Spoon the batter into the pan. Bake until golden, 15 to 20 minutes.

Serve with butter.

Blueberry Muffins

yields 24 miniature muffins

An American classic. I adapted this recipe from Beth Hensperger's *Muffins*, replacing processed ingredients with whole foods. In miniature, these muffins are just adorable. They make a lovely accompaniment for afternoon tea or Sunday breakfast.

3/4 stick (90 g) butter
1/2 cup (120 ml) agave nectar or maple syrup
zest of 1 lemon
2 eggs
1 pinch salt
1 3/4 cups (420 ml) whole-wheat flour
2 teaspoons baking powder
3/4 cup (180 ml) kefir or yogurt
1 1/2 teaspoons vanilla extract
4 1/2 ounces (125 g) fresh or frozen blueberries (if frozen, do not thaw)

1. Preheat the oven to 400°F (200°C).
2. Butter a pan for 24 miniature muffins.
3. Whip the butter. Stir in the agave nectar, zest, eggs and salt and mix well.
4. Combine the flour and baking powder.
5. Add the flour mixture, kefir and vanilla into the egg mixture. Mix well.
6. Very carefully stir in the blueberries, trying not to break any.
7. Spoon the batter into the pan. Bake until golden, 10 to 15 minutes.

Serve with tea.

Dressings and Spreads

Dressings

Here are a few lovely salad dressings that are simple and easy to make. The basic ingredients for a sensible dressing are always an oil and an acidic component such as lemon juice or vinegar – the oil helps your body absorb the fat-soluble vitamins in your salad and the acid component draws extra calcium out of the greens. Add dressing just before serving. The lettuce in any salad wilts when it sits in dressing for a long time.

One practical way of making salad dressings is to combine all ingredients in a glass jar with a lid. It is convenient to mix the dressing by shaking the closed jar, and you have a good container in which to store any extra dressing. Make more than you need for one salad and store the rest for up to a week in the refrigerator.

Experiment with different oils, vinegars and herbs. Try sherry vinegar, raspberry vinegar, apple cider vinegar or rice vinegar. A favorite of mine is umeboshi vinegar, which technically is not a vinegar but the brine of lacto-fermented umeboshi plums, a Japanese delicacy. It is quite salty and has a fruity tartness to it. For your oil, try hazelnut oil, walnut oil or pumpkin seed oil. Add different fresh herbs such as parsley, dill, cilantro and basil, or dried herbs such as thyme, tarragon and oregano. Finely chopped ginger gives a nice kick to any dressing and so does pressed garlic.

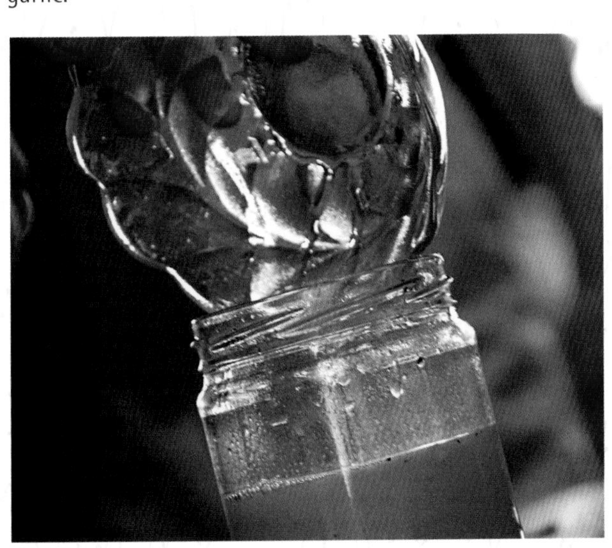

Very Basic Dressing

½ cup (120 ml) olive oil
¼ cup (60 ml) red balsamic vinegar
2 tablespoons soy sauce

Tarragon Dressing

½ cup (120 ml) olive oil
¼ cup (60 ml) red balsamic vinegar
2 pinches dried tarragon
1 clove garlic, pressed

Note: Tarragon is one herb that I prefer to use dried. I find it much more fragrant when it is dried.

Roasted Sesame Dressing

4 tablespoons roasted sesame oil
3 tablespoons white balsamic vinegar
2 tablespoons soy sauce
1 tablespoon maple syrup
¼ teaspoon chili pepper flakes

Grapefruit Dressing

½ cup (120 ml) olive oil
¼ cup (60 ml) grapefruit juice
1 clove garlic, pressed
1 to 2 teaspoons maple syrup
1 pinch salt

Honey Mustard Dressing

½ cup (120 ml) olive oil
¼ cup (60 ml) lemon juice
1 to 2 teaspoons prepared mustard
1 to 2 teaspoons honey

Note: This dressing is featured in the salad on page 224.

Lemon Soy Dressing

serves 6

A lovely, tangy dressing with kicks of garlic and ginger. People always ask, "What is in that dressing?"

- 2 cloves garlic, pressed
- 1 piece fresh ginger, about 1½ inches (4 cm) long, peeled and chopped fine
- juice of 2 lemons
- ¼ cup (60 ml) olive oil
- ¼ cup (60 ml) soy sauce
- 1 tablespoon snipped chives (optional)

Combine all ingredients in a glass jar. Close the lid and shake well to mix.

This dressing goes well with cooked grains, vegetables and leafy greens. It is featured in the steamed vegetable recipe on page 80.

Yogurt Dressing

serves 6

The combination of cumin and lime makes this cooling dressing interesting.

- 1 teaspoon ground cumin
- ½ teaspoon cayenne pepper
- 2 cups (480 ml) yogurt
- juice of 1 lime
- ½ teaspoon honey
- salt

Combine all ingredients in a bowl and mix well.

This dressing goes well with vegetables and especially well with bean dishes, as the friendly bacteria in the yogurt help with digestion.

Tahini Dressing

serves 4 to 6

Tahini and roasted sesame oil impart a lovely nutty taste to this creamy dressing.

3 tablespoons tahini (sesame butter)
3 tablespoons water
1 tablespoon roasted sesame oil
juice of ½ lemon
1 tablespoon maple syrup
1 tablespoon soy sauce

Combine the tahini and water in a bowl. Stir until the mixture is smooth. At first it will seem as though the tahini is not going to combine with the water. Keep on stirring and it will. When the mixture is smooth, add the other ingredients and mix well.

Serve with vegetables, greens or cooked grains.

Note: Never use roasted sesame oil as cooking oil. It is meant to be used as a flavoring. Include it in dressings or sprinkle it over stir-fries at the end of the cooking process.

Parsley Dressing

serves 4 to 6

This is an intensely green dressing and an intense taste sensation!

6 handfuls parsley leaves
1 piece fresh ginger, 1½ inches (4 cm) long, cut into small pieces
2 cloves garlic
juice of ½ lemon
½ cup (120 ml) olive or walnut oil
1 to 2 tablespoons soy sauce

Place all ingredients into blender and puree.

Serve with steamed vegetables or cooked grains. I love it poured over polenta (page 112).

Hummus

serves 4

This Middle Eastern spread is highly nutritious and delicious. Chickpeas have the highest iron and calcium content of all legumes.

1 can (15 ounces or 420 g) chickpeas, drained and rinsed
1 handful parsley leaves
1 scallion, chopped coarse
1 or 2 cloves garlic
juice of ½ to 1 lemon
3 to 4 tablespoons water
2 tablespoons olive oil
2 tablespoons soy sauce
1 pinch cayenne pepper

Place all ingredients in a blender or food processor and puree.

Serve as a dip for raw vegetables or as a vegan spread on toasted whole-grain bread.

Onion Butter

Butter in this context refers to a spread that is made purely from one ingredient by cooking it over low heat for a long, long time. No water, no fat, no sweetener gets added. Because of the long cooking time, the natural sugars of the solo ingredient are released. I promise this onion butter will be a revelation. It tastes so sweet that it can pass as jam.

8 onions, chopped coarse

1. Place the onions in a large pot and cook over the lowest possible heat for 6 to 8 hours. Stir once in a while.
2. For a smoother consistency, spoon the cooked onions into a blender or food processor and puree.
3. Transfer to a bowl and allow to cool.

Serve with Karask (page 198), whole-grain bread or crackers.

Variation: You can prepare apple, pear or plum butter in the same manner.

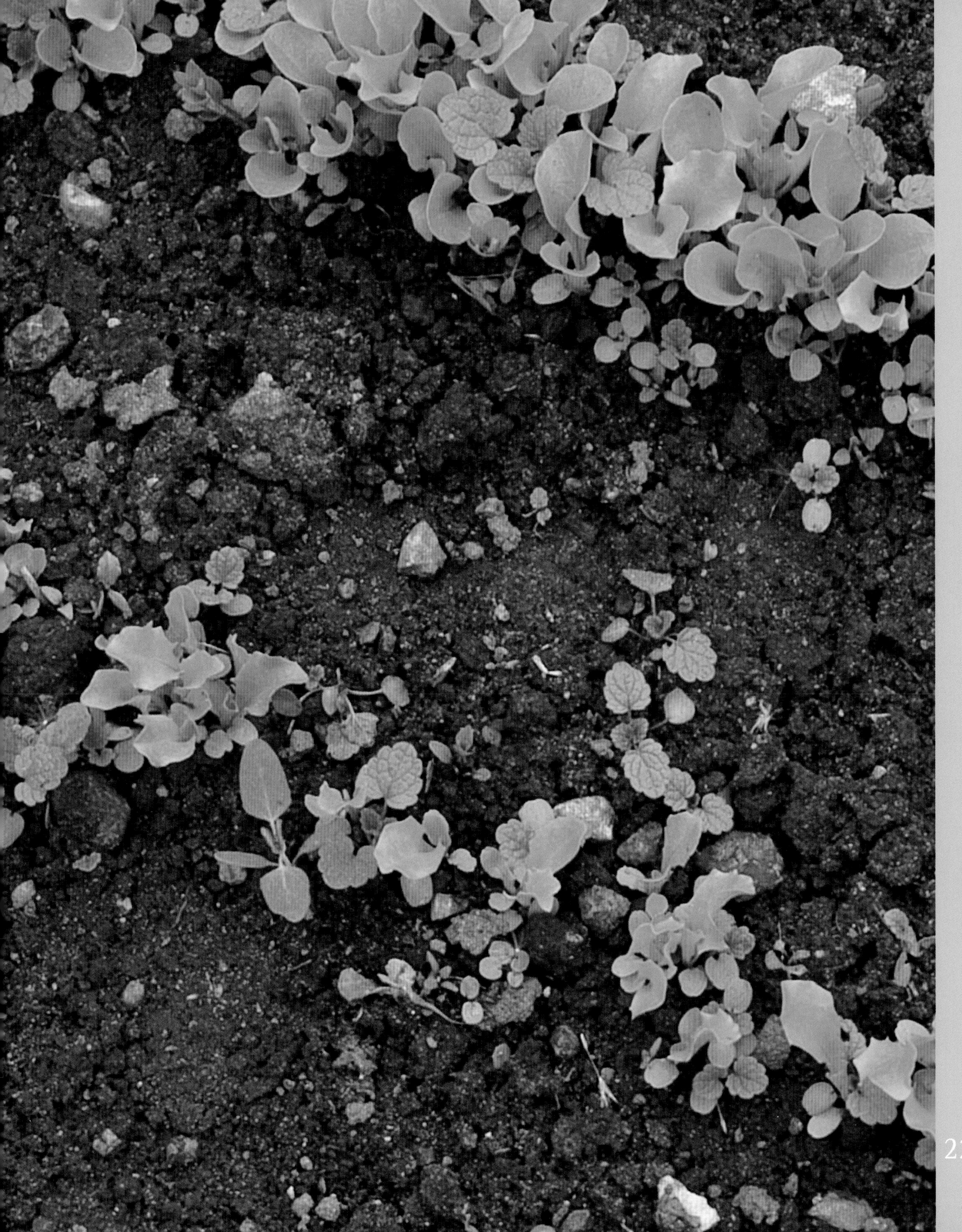

Green Salad with Goat Cheese, Cashews and Pears

serves 4

This is my re-creation of a lovely salad I had at a Miami Beach restaurant.

Salad:

½ cup (120 ml) raw cashews

4 handfuls lettuce, different varieties including arugula

1 or 2 pears, quartered lengthwise, seeds removed, then cut crosswise into thin slices

4 ounces (115 g) soft goat cheese, cut into chunks

Dressing:

½ cup (120 ml) olive oil

¼ cup (60 ml) lemon juice

1 to 2 teaspoons prepared mustard

1 to 2 teaspoons honey

1. Preheat the oven to 400°F (200°C).
2. Spread the cashews on a cookie sheet or in a baking dish and roast for 5 minutes or until light brown. Be careful not to burn the nuts – once you smell the aroma, they are done.
3. Tear the lettuce into bite-size pieces and submerge in cold water. Move the lettuce around in the water to dislodge any soil or sand. Drain in a colander or use a salad spinner.
4. Arrange the lettuce on a large platter. Add the pear slices and the cheese. Top with the roasted cashews.
5. Place all dressing ingredients into a glass jar. Close the lid and shake to mix. Just before serving, pour the dressing evenly over the salad.

Serve with whole-wheat toast and butter.

Greek Salad à la Polli

serves 4

This is a lovely salad for a hot summer day. Instead of the customary iceberg lettuce, we use Chinese cabbage, which is a lot more flavorful and much more nutritious. Iceberg lettuce is about the least nutritious food that grows in a garden.

1 Chinese cabbage, cut into bite-size pieces
4 tomatoes, cut lengthwise into wedges, then cut crosswise
1 long cucumber, peeled and cubed
2 medium red onions, quartered lengthwise, then sliced into very thin crescents
½ cup (120 ml) pitted kalamata olives
3 tablespoons olive oil
1 tablespoon dried thyme
pepper
9 ounces (250 g) feta cheese, cubed

1. Combine the vegetables in a bowl.
2. Add the olives, oil, thyme and pepper to taste. Mix well.
3. Just prior to serving, add the feta and toss gently.

Serve with crisp bread and butter.

Carrot Salad with Pumpkin Seeds

serves 4

This is a great salad inspired by a recipe from the Institute for Integrative Nutrition. It looks beautiful and is intensely pleasurable, especially with organic carrots. You can easily transport this colorful treat to any picnic or potluck.

Salad:

1 pound (500 g) carrots
1/4 cup (60 ml) dried cranberries
1/4 cup (60 ml) pumpkin seeds
1 handful parsley leaves, chopped

Dressing:

1 piece ginger root, 2 inches (5 cm) long, grated fine
2 to 3 tablespoons apple cider vinegar
2 pinches salt
4 tablespoons olive oil

1. Grate the carrots and place them into a bowl. Stir in the cranberries, pumpkin seeds and parsley.
2. Using your fingers, press the juice from the grated ginger into a glass jar.
3. Add the vinegar, salt and oil. Close the lid and shake to mix.

Pour the dressing over the salad and toss.

Root Vegetable Vinaigrette

serves 4

The beet turns this vinaigrette a vibrant magenta, and the dish provides a gorgeous color accent for any occasion.

Vegetables:

1 beet, peeled and cubed
2 carrots, sliced into rounds
1 turnip, peeled and cubed
1 parsnip, peeled and sliced into rounds

Dressing:

3 tablespoons olive oil
3 tablespoons red balsamic vinegar
salt and pepper
1 handful chopped scallions
1 handful chopped basil

1. Fill a pot with 1 inch (2½ cm) of water, insert a steamer basket and bring the water to a boil.
2. Add the vegetables – start with the beet, then add the carrots, then the turnip, then the parsnip – waiting three minutes after each addition. Steam until the vegetables start to get soft. Transfer the vegetables to a colander, rinse with cold water and drain. Transfer to a bowl.
3. Combine the dressing ingredients in a glass jar. Close the lid and shake to mix. Pour the dressing over the vegetables, mix well, and let the salad marinate for at least 1 hour.
4. Before serving, toss, taste and add vinegar or seasoning if needed.

Garnish with basil leaves.

Note: You can use just about any vegetable in this recipe – it is also a great way to make vegetable leftovers taste delicious the next day.

Kilu Casserole

serves 6

In Estonia we have a delicacy called *kilu.* Kilu are little fish, similar to sardines. They are prepared raw, salted and marinated in a particular mixture of spices. Outside of Estonia where kilu are unavailable, substitute anchovies or herring.

6 to 10 potatoes, peeled and cut into 1/4-inch (1/2-cm) slices
2 to 3 onions, cut lengthwise in half, then sliced into crescents
7 ounces (200 g) kilu fillets
2 cups (480 ml) heavy cream
salt and pepper

1. Preheat the oven to 450°F (250°C).
2. Place a layer of the potato slices in a 8 x 12-inch (20 x 30-cm) baking dish.
3. Add a layer of onions and then a layer of kilu. Sprinkle with pepper.
4. Repeat with layers of potatoes, onions and kilu. Sprinkle with additional pepper.
5. Top with a layer of potatoes.
6. Pour in the cream and sprinkle with a little salt.
7. Cover with aluminum foil and bake for 1 hour.
8. Remove the aluminum foil and bake until the potatoes turn brown, another 15 to 30 minutes.

Serve with pickled cucumbers and a shot of ice-cold vodka.

Note: If you use a smaller, deeper baking dish, you can add more layers. The top layer should always be potatoes.

Baked Salmon Fillet

serves 6

This is a very simple way of baking salmon, trout or char that really brings out the flavor of the fish in a Zen kind of way.

2½ pounds (1 kg) salmon fillet with skin intact
salt and pepper
2 lemons, sliced in cross sections, seeds removed

1. Preheat the oven to 450°F (250°C).
2. Arrange the fish, skin side down, in a large baking dish or pan.
3. Sprinkle with salt and pepper. Top with pairs of lemon rounds aligned down the center of the fillet.
4. Add a little water to the dish and bake for 20 minutes.

Serve with boiled potatoes and a leafy green or other vegetable.

Note: The lemon rounds give the fish a subtle taste of lemon. They also make a beautiful presentation and are helpful in dividing the fish into portions. Everybody gets two lemon rounds. If you are serving six, there should be twelve lemon rounds covering the fish.

Lox in Sour Cream Sauce

serves 6

This is a quick and easy pasta dish that requires very little cooking time, as all ingredients in the sauce need only to be heated. Cooking the pasta will take the longest.

Pasta:

1 pound (500 g) whole-grain penne
salt and olive oil

Sauce:

2 cups (500 g) sour cream
2 cups (480 ml) halved cherry tomatoes
9 ounces (250 g) salted lox, cut into strips
salt and pepper
1 bunch dill, snipped fine

1. Cook the penne according to instructions on the package, adding some salt and olive oil to the cooking water. Drain the cooked pasta.
2. In a separate pot, bring the sour cream to a light boil. Add the tomatoes and simmer until the tomatoes are heated through.
3. Add the lox. Cook only until the lox is heated through.
4. Add salt and pepper to taste – if the lox is very salty, do not add salt.
5. Just before serving, stir in the dill. Pour the sauce over the cooked pasta and toss gently.

Serve with a green salad.

Shrimp with Leeks in Cream Sauce

serves 6

This recipe dates back to the year after I finished high school, which I spent in Borås, Sweden. Ann Granquist, my classmate at the Textile Institute there, prepared the dish. I fell deeply in love with it and have been cooking it for more than thirty years. Ann made it with Worcestershire sauce, which I eventually came to exclude for a purer taste experience. It is a great recipe for guests because you can prep everything in advance and then cook it up in four minutes.

2 cups (480 ml) heavy cream
6 leeks, cut into ½-inch (1-cm) pieces
11 ounces (300 g) shrimp, cooked and shelled
salt and pepper
cayenne pepper

1. Combine the cream and leeks in a pot and bring to a boil. Reduce the heat and cook just until the leeks turn bright green, 2 to 4 minutes.
2. Add the shrimp and cook just until they are heated through. Overcooking will make the shrimp tough.
3. Stir in salt, pepper and cayenne pepper to taste.

Serve over brown rice or quinoa.

Chicken Legs with Prunes and Almonds

serves 4

Most people love chicken, so this is an easy crowd-pleaser.

4 chicken thighs with drumsticks
salt and pepper
paprika
cayenne pepper
1 onion, cut into wedges
4 cloves garlic, sliced
½ cup (120 ml) pitted prunes
⅓ cup (80 ml) almonds

1. Preheat the oven to 450°F (250°C).
2. Trim excess fat from the chicken parts. Rinse and pat them dry with paper towels and sprinkle with the salt, pepper, paprika and cayenne pepper.
3. Spread the onion and garlic in a baking dish large enough to hold the chicken.
4. Place the chicken on top of the onion and garlic. Arrange the prunes and almonds between the chicken pieces. Add ½ inch (1 cm) of water. Bake for 40 to 45 minutes.
5. Carefully tilt the dish and spoon out as much of the cooking liquid as possible to use as a sauce, adjusting seasoning if needed.
6. Keep the sauce hot and spoon over the chicken when serving.

Serve with brown rice and vegetables.

Variation: Substitute dried apricots for the prunes.

Chicken Breast in Coconut Milk

serves 6

This is a lovely dish inspired by Thai cuisine. I love the combination of coconut milk and basil.

1 medium onion, chopped
9 ounces (250 g) chanterelle, shitake or champignon mushrooms, sliced
2 tablespoons olive oil
salt and pepper
1 pound (500 g) green beans, ends trimmed, cut into 2-inch (5-cm) pieces

2 breasts of chicken, boneless and skinless, cut into 1/4-inch (1/2-cm) slices
salt and pepper
paprika
cayenne pepper
2 tablespoons coconut oil

12 basil leaves, chopped coarse
1 can (14 ounces or 415 ml) coconut milk

1. Sauté the onion and mushrooms in the oil for 7 to 10 minutes. Add salt and pepper to taste.
2. Steam the green beans until tender, 7 to 10 minutes.
3. Rub the spices on the chicken pieces and sauté in the oil for 2 minutes on each side.
4. In a pot, combine the mushroom sauté, steamed green beans and cooked chicken. Add the basil and coconut milk. Bring to a boil, then reduce the heat and simmer for 10 minutes. Adjust seasoning if needed.

Serve over cooked quinoa or brown rice.

Variation: Try different vegetables, or substitute shrimp for chicken.

Fruits

What we call fruits in common parlance are the succulent fruits, the sweet, juicy, delicious, sensuous sugary fruits. The Latin root *frui* tells it like it is: "to enjoy or delight in." While grains, legumes, nuts and seeds are fruits whose skins harden as they mature, the succulent fruits have soft or fleshy skins. Several vegetables are, botanically speaking, actually fruits: tomatoes, peppers, eggplants, avocados and all members of the squash family such as winter squash, zucchini, cucumber and pumpkin. I will focus here on the succulent fruits and continue to call them simply fruits.

Fruits in general have cooling energy. You will find the most cooling fruits in the tropics, where they grow year-round and serve to bring the eater some relief from the hot climate. Fruits from moderate climates grow only in the summer and are best eaten in season.

Fruits are very high in fructose, a simple carbohydrate (or monosaccharide). They are relatively high in potassium and vitamin C, and they contain some enzymes, phytochemicals and fiber but not too many minerals. They contain no fat or protein.

While fruits are certainly a more healthful choice when it comes to sugary foods, eating too much fruit can also destabilize blood sugar levels. Fruits are a great source of quick energy, but they are not cell-building or restorative foods. They can be the perfect balancing food for hot-blooded, physically very active people – those with pitta-type bodies – considering their lifestyle and personality (see page 33). For the easily cold and weaker in physique vata types, fruit is best eaten in moderation, because of both its cooling effect and its high sugar content. For vatas, too much fruit can diminish vitality and weaken the entire system.

Baking or cooking fruit can reduce its cooling effect. Adding warming spices such as cinnamon and ginger helps to reduce the cooling effect as well. Cooking and spicing fruit makes sense in the colder months when we might not really need cooling.

To best absorb the nutrients in fruits, eat them by themselves, not combined with other foods. They are digested more quickly than are most other foods.

Among the fruits, berries have a special status as "superfoods" (see page 283).

Natural Sweeteners

I highly recommend using natural sweeteners instead of white table sugar. Natural sweeteners do not cause surges and dips in blood sugar. They do not cause destabilizing swings in energy and mood or present the health risks caused by white sugar.

Natural sweeteners are gentler on the body than are highly processed sugars. They do not overtax the pancreas, and they allow continuous glucagon production, which in turn allows fat to be burned for energy (see page 26).

Natural sweeteners, unlike white sugar and corn syrup, are not empty foods. They do not rob our bodies of minerals. While their sugar content is high, natural sweeteners do provide in concentrated form all of the minerals contained in the plants they were derived from, and in the case of honey, all of the enzymes that the bees produce. However, please do not overindulge in natural sweeteners either – use them in moderation. After all, they do have concentrated sugar content, which can cause dental caries, weaken our immune system and set the stage for many diseases.

Substituting natural sweeteners for white sugar in baking will take some experimentation and some trial and error. Because most natural sweeteners are syrups, they add a liquid quality, so you need to adjust the quantities of other liquids in a recipe.

Instead of adjusting any existing recipes that call for white sugar, you might want to start by trying new recipes that already include natural sweeteners as ingredients – such as those in this cookbook!

I encourage you to experiment with some of the following natural sweeteners:

Honey is mostly fructose and glucose. It is not just a sweetener – it has medicinal properties as well, being antiseptic and antibacterial. It contains small amounts of minerals, vitamins, antioxidants and enzymes. To preserve honey's enzymes and healing properties, avoid heating it above 117°F (47°C). Look for honey labeled "raw," and try to use honey in desserts that do not require heating or baking. Crystallization is a natural process that occurs in honey – if it does not crystallize, it has probably been heated in the harvesting process and its quality is therefore compromised.

Maple syrup is mostly sucrose, a disaccharide composed of fructose and glucose. It is the concentrated sap of maple trees, so it is rich in trace minerals brought up from deep below the earth by the trees' far-reaching root systems. It imparts a wonderful flavor and can be used in baking and in porridge. Make sure to buy 100 percent pure maple syrup, not maple-flavored corn syrup.

Agave nectar is made from the juice of the agave plant, a succulent that grows in the American Southwest, Mexico and Central America. Its naturally high fructose content does not lead to a sugar surge. Because of its low glycemic load, it can be enjoyed in moderation even by diabetics. It is sweeter than refined sugar and has a neutral sweet taste. You do not need much, and the flavor of your food will not be changed by any distinctive taste, as it would with honey or maple syrup. Use it in baking and for sweetening yogurt and drinks. When purchasing agave nectar, make sure the product is made from the juice of the agave plant and not the starch of its root – the process of making the sweetener from the starch of the root is similar to that of making corn syrup.

Brown rice syrup is the result of mixing ground and cooked brown rice with enzymes. Some of the starch is broken down into maltose, a disaccharide composed of two glucose molecules. The end product still contains 50 percent complex carbohydrates and 43 percent maltose. Brown rice syrup has a lovely, moderately sweet taste. When replacing white sugar with brown rice syrup, you might need to add up to 50 percent more.

Barley malt is the dark-brown, mildly sweet thick syrup that results when sprouted barley is fermented. Bacteria transform the starches into sugars, mostly maltose. It contains about 30 percent complex carbohydrates and 65 percent maltose. You might need to add a larger quantity of barley malt in your recipes when substituting for white sugar.

Sugar cane products include dehydrated cane juice, blackstrap molasses, brown sugar and turbinado sugar. Of these, I recommend only dehydrated cane juice and blackstrap molasses. The others are basically 99 percent white sugar with a little molasses coating on the surface of the sugar crystals.

Dehydrated cane juice, used in India for thousands of years, is rich in minerals, especially silica. The sugar cane is squeezed, then the juice is filtered, boiled and dried. This is the least processed sugar cane product.

Blackstrap molasses is the most nutritious sweetener derived from sugar cane. It is the residual syrup that remains at the very end of sugar extraction. It is very dark in color and has a distinct taste. It contains the lowest sugar content of the sugar cane derivatives and the highest vitamin and mineral content, providing potassium, iron, calcium, magnesium and vitamin B6. Look for unsulphured blackstrap molasses.

Stevia, in a class of its own, is a sweet powder made from the South American honey leaf plant. Stevioside and rebaudioside, both glycosides, are the chemical compounds that give stevia its sweet taste. Just a pinch of stevia provides the sweetness of a spoonful of sugar. Because it does not add bulk, it is difficult to use as a sugar substitute in baking. But it does work well in dressings, smoothies and drinks. Stevia is a remarkable product: it has zero calories, contains a host of minerals, does not affect blood sugar levels at all, lowers elevated blood pressure and improves digestion. Stevia is an excellent choice for diabetics and for people with candida. The only drawback is a slightly bitter aftertaste.

Another way of adding sweetness to your desserts, baked things, and porridges is to add raisins or other dried fruits (pages 210 and 266). In the same way, I like to add sweetness to grain salads (pages 114 and 120), soups (page 192), leafy greens – especially the ones with a bitter taste (page 140), and even chicken (page 242).

A word on **corn syrup** (also called **glucose syrup**) and high-fructose corn syrup: While its name sounds innocent and natural, corn syrup is a heavily processed artificial product containing highly reactive forms of glucose and fructose. It can cause tissue damage and high triglyceride levels in the blood – a condition that is a heart disease risk factor.

It has been said that corn syrup also programs the brain for an intense desire for sweets. That desire can lead to a lifelong overconsumption of sweets, increasing the risk of obesity, diabetes and related health problems. Please read labels carefully and try to avoid products containing corn syrup in any form.

Finally, a word on **artificial sweeteners**, such as aspartame, saccharin, sucralose, acesulfame K (or acesulfame potassium) and neotame: Please stay away from all artificial sweeteners and all diet and sugar-free products that contain these sweeteners. Many are carcinogens, and some are neurotoxins.

Desserts and Sweets

Rye Rhubarb Mousse

serves 10 to 12

This is a traditional Estonian dessert. To anybody but an Estonian, this mousse made of rye must seem rather perplexing. But Estonians have long been successful at making fluffy desserts from grain. My mom used to make a similar dessert using cream of wheat and red currant juice. I got to taste the rye mousse – from Helle Veltman's kitchen – for the first time a few summers ago. Rhubarb is one of the first edible things you can harvest from your garden, so enjoy this dessert in late spring.

3 cups (400 g) rhubarb chunks (stalks peeled and cut into ½-inch (1-cm) pieces)
3 cups (720 ml) water
8 to 10 tablespoons maple syrup or agave nectar
½ teaspoon ground cinnamon
1 pinch salt
¾ cup (180 ml) rye flour
lemon balm leaves or berries

1. Boil the rhubarb in the water until it becomes soft and loses its structure. Add the maple syrup, cinnamon and salt.
2. Slowly whisk in the rye flour. Bring to a boil, continuously whisking, then reduce the heat to low and simmer for 5 minutes.
3. Allow to cool. With a hand mixer, whip the mixture until its volume has doubled.
4. Pour the mousse into individual dessert dishes and garnish with a lemon balm leaf or berries.

Serve as is, or with milk or whipped cream.

Blueberries and Cream

serves 6

This is one of our favorite summer desserts at the farm – and our simplest. It is divine!

6 cups (600 g) wild blueberries
1 cup (240 ml) heavy cream
1 teaspoon vanilla extract (optional)
maple syrup

1. Divide the blueberries into 6 individual dessert bowls.
2. Whip the cream together with the vanilla until firm.
3. Top the blueberries with the whipped cream and a drizzle of maple syrup.

Alegría – Mexican Amaranth Candy

serves 8

Looking for a recipe that utilizes amaranth, I came across this traditional Mexican candy in Rebecca Wood's *The Splendid Grain*. It is a little more complicated than our other sweets, but well worth the effort. Read the entire recipe before you begin.

- 1/4 cup (60 ml) sunflower seeds
- 1/2 cup (120 ml) amaranth
- 1/3 cup (80 ml) brown rice syrup
- 1/2 teaspoon ground cinnamon
- 1 pinch salt

1. Preheat the oven to 400°F (200°C).
2. Spread the sunflower seeds on a cookie sheet or in a baking dish and roast for about 5 minutes. When you smell the aroma, they are done. Set aside.
3. Prepare popped amaranth: heat a pot with high sides and add 1/4 cup (60 ml) of the amaranth. Keep over medium heat, stirring continuously until most of the kernels have popped and those that have not are light brown.
4. Pour the popped amaranth into a bowl and repeat the procedure with the remaining 1/4 cup (60 ml) of amaranth.
5. Cover a work surface with a 20-inch (50-cm) piece of parchment paper.
6. Bring the brown rice syrup to a boil. Reduce the heat and cook for 10 minutes, being careful not to burn the syrup. The color of the rice syrup should not change.
7. Remove from the heat and stir in the roasted sunflower seeds, cinnamon and salt. Stir in the popped amaranth.
8. Pour the mixture onto half of the parchment paper. With the other half, cover the mixture and press to flatten it to an even thickness. When cool, cut into 1 x 2-inch (2 x 5-cm) rectangular bars.

Note: This recipe requires that you are well organized and quick. Have all items set up and ready to go. The brown rice syrup needs to boil long enough to harden once it cools down. If you do not boil it for a full ten minutes, it will stay elastic and sticky. Once the brown rice syrup is boiled, you need to mix and spread the mass quickly. Don't wait too long to cut the bars, as the mass quickly becomes too brittle to cut.

Potent Round Brownies

makes 18 - 24 individual brownies

I found a brownie recipe on the Institute for Integrative Nutrition website. It called for carob powder. For a chocolate lover like me, that was unacceptable. How can you make a brownie with a chocolate substitute? So I tweaked the recipe to include high-quality chocolate (preferably sweetened with evaporated cane juice) and a pinch of cayenne pepper. Both cacao and cayenne pepper are aphrodisiacs. Cayenne pepper also dilates capillaries and thus allows cacao's abundant nutrients to reach cells more easily. The other surprise in this brownie recipe is that it uses chickpeas or black beans instead of flour. Remember the role of legumes (page 149) when it comes to strengthening the kidneys and helping to restore vitality and sexual energy? Now you know why I call these potent brownies.

- 10½ ounces (300 g) dark chocolate (70 percent cacao)
- 2 cans (15 ounces or 420 g each) chickpeas or black beans, drained and rinsed
- 4 eggs
- ⅔ cup (160 ml) agave nectar or maple syrup
- ½ teaspoon baking powder
- 1 teaspoon vanilla extract
- 1 pinch cayenne pepper
- 1 pinch salt

1. Preheat the oven to 400°F (200°C). Butter two pans for 12 standard-size muffins
2. Break the chocolate into pieces and melt by placing the pieces in a heat-resistant bowl inside a pot of boiling water, or use a double boiler.
3. Combine the beans and eggs in a blender or food processor.
4. Add the agave nectar, baking powder, vanilla, cayenne pepper and salt. Blend until smooth.
5. Transfer the mixture into a bowl. Stir in the melted chocolate.
6. Spoon the batter into muffin cups and bake for 15 minutes.
7. Allow to cool before serving.

Note: For a special treat – on Valentine's Day, for example – garnish individual brownies with whipped cream and a strawberry. Read more about cacao in the chapter on superfoods (page 284).

Plum Cake

serves 8

This cake is inspired by a recipe from my dear friend Marika Mann. In Estonia, there is an expression that translates into English as a "company dish" – something you make often that always turns out great. This cake is definitely Marika's "company cake." She makes different versions using a variety of berries and fruits. One version I enjoy features raspberries. The first time Marika came to visit the farm was on our first Open House day in 1999. She arrived, looked around, seemed positively surprised, and said, "I think I need to go home and bake a cake for you." She returned later in the afternoon with a large pan full of her company cake, and if I remember correctly, she used black currants that time.

Crust:

1 1/8 sticks (125 g) butter
1/3 cup (120 ml) whole-wheat flour
1/3 cup (120 ml) rye flour
1/3 cup (120 ml) barley flour
1/2 teaspoon baking powder
3 tablespoons maple syrup
1 pinch salt

Filling:

6 to 8 plums, cut in half, pitted
1 cup (250 g) sour cream
1 egg
2 or 3 tablespoons maple syrup
2 teaspoons vanilla extract
1 pinch salt
1/2 cup (120 ml) almond slivers

1. Preheat the oven to 400°F (200°C).
2. Whip the butter. In a separate bowl, combine the flours and baking powder.
3. Gradually stir the flour mixture into the butter. Add the maple syrup and salt. Mix until the dough becomes uniform.
4. Cover the bottom and sides of a quiche dish or springform pan (10 inches or 25 cm in diameter) with the dough.
5. Place the plums, skin side up, on the dough.
6. Combine the sour cream, egg, maple syrup, vanilla and salt. Pour the mixture carefully around the plums on the dough so that the plums remain visible.
7. Sprinkle with the almond slivers and bake until the filling is set, 40 to 60 minutes.

Pumpkin Pie

serves 8

In the States, this American classic always accompanies Thanksgiving dinner and often Christmas dinner as well. The combination of spices definitely places it in the winter season.

Crust:

1 cup (240 ml) whole-wheat flour
1/4 teaspoon baking powder
1/2 teaspoon salt
3/4 stick (85 g) chilled butter, cut into 6 pieces
2 to 4 tablespoons cold water

Filling:

2 cups (480 ml) pumpkin puree (see note)
1/2 teaspoon peeled and grated ginger
1/2 teaspoon ground cinnamon
1/2 teaspoon ground cloves
1/2 teaspoon salt
2 eggs
1/3 cup (80 ml) maple syrup
1/2 cup (120 ml) sour cream

1. Combine the flour, baking powder and salt. Add the butter and mix. Add the water 1 tablespoon at a time and continue to mix, forming a kneadable dough.
2. Roll the dough into a ball, then press it into a disc shape. Wrap the dough in plastic wrap and refrigerate for 30 minutes.
3. Combine the pumpkin puree with the ginger, cinnamon, cloves, salt, eggs, maple syrup and sour cream.
4. Preheat the oven to 400°F (200°C). Butter a 9- or 10-inch (24-cm) pie plate.
5. Turn the pie plate upside down on a sheet of parchment paper and trace the perimeter of the rim onto the paper. Remove the plate and place the dough on the paper in the center of the circle. Roll out the dough to the size of the circle. Using the paper as a base, turn the dough into the pie plate. Carefully peel away the paper and let the dough settle into the plate – it should cover the bottom and sides.
6. Pinch any excess dough into a decorative edge. Prick the dough on the bottom with a fork.
7. Pour the filling into the crust and bake until the filling is set, 50 to 55 minutes.

Serve as is or with whipped cream.

Variation: Instead of pumpkin, use sweet potatoes – reduce the amount of maple syrup to 1/4 cup (60 ml), as sweet potatoes are very sweet themselves.

Note: To make the pumpkin puree, cut a small pumpkin into quarters and scrape out the seeds and fibrous parts. Cut each quarter into large chunks and steam until tender, around 20 minutes. Remove the pumpkin from the steamer and save the cooking water. When the cooked pumpkin is cool, peel each chunk and place it into the bowl of a food processor. Puree until smooth, adding a small amount of the cooking water if needed. Use any leftover puree for soups (pages 192 and 194).

Apple Cranberry Hazelnut Crisp

serves 10

A classic American recipe. There is something very satisfying about the combination of apples, cinnamon and oats. The cranberries add a little zing, and the aroma of the baked hazelnuts is irresistible.

Filling:

½ cup (120 ml) apple cider or juice
1½ teaspoons cornstarch
¼ cup (60 ml) maple syrup
1 teaspoon ground cinnamon
1 teaspoon vanilla extract
1 pinch salt
9 tart apples, hearts and seeds removed, cut into small chunks
½ cup (120 ml) cranberries, halved

Crust:

1½ cups (360 ml) rolled oats
½ cup (120 ml) whole-wheat flour
1 cup (240 ml) hazelnuts, halved
⅓ cup (80 ml) maple syrup
½ stick (50 g) butter, cut into slices
1 teaspoon ground cinnamon
1 teaspoon vanilla extract
½ teaspoon salt

1. Butter a 9 x 12-inch (22 x 30-cm) baking pan. Preheat the oven to 400°F (200°C).
2. Pour the cider into a bowl and combine with the cornstarch. Stir in the remaining filling ingredients.
3. Combine the crust ingredients in a separate bowl.
4. Pour the filling mixture into the baking pan. Distribute the crust mixture over the filling.
5. Cover with aluminum foil and bake for 50 minutes.
6. Remove the aluminum foil and continue to bake until the crust is crunchy and the juices of the filling are thick and bubbly, another 10 minutes.

Serve as is or with whipped cream, sour cream or vanilla ice cream.

Variation: Substitute lingonberries for the cranberries.

Coconut Prune Cookies

yields about 30 cookies

I experimented with this recipe before including it in my cooking weekend one summer. The cookies were an instant hit, and I bake them often. They are meant to be moist and soft – if you store them in an airtight container, they will stay that way.

20 prunes, pitted
½ cup (120 ml) water
½ cup (120 ml) maple syrup
½ cup (120 ml) olive oil
2 pinches salt
1 cup (240 ml) rolled oats
1 cup (240 ml) coconut flakes (unsweetened)
1 cup (240 ml) whole-wheat flour
½ teaspoon baking powder

1. Soak the prunes in the water for 30 minutes. Reserve the soaking water.
2. Preheat the oven to 400°F (200°C).
3. In a blender, puree the soaked prunes, soaking water, maple syrup, oil and salt.
4. Pour the mixture into a bowl and stir in the oats, coconut, flour and baking powder.
5. Line a cookie sheet with parchment paper. Form the dough into little balls and flatten them onto the cookie sheet. Each cookie should be about 2 inches (5 cm) in diameter.
6. Bake for 15 minutes.

Drinks

Water Dressed Up

There are many ways to make water more interesting – even festive – both in taste and presentation. Lime or cucumber slices, peppermint or lemon balm leaves, rose petals or strawberries are just a few items you can add to a pitcher or glass to infuse your water with gentle nuances.

Herbal Teas

At the farm, we like to end dinner with a soothing cup of herbal tea. During the summer months, we take fresh leaves or flowers straight from the garden, without drying the plants. I find that teas made with fresh leaves or blossoms have a milder, more subtle taste.

Some cultivated fresh herbs that are suitable for tea are peppermint, lemon balm, thyme, sage and calendula – these grow right in my garden. Black currant, raspberry and strawberry leaves make great teas as well. And then there are wild flowers and herbs such as cowslip, which blooms in May, and wild thyme, St. John's wort and linden flowers, which bloom in July. My neighbor Helgi Reeder has a beautiful linden tree that provides us with lovely flowers for tea.

Simply place a few leaves or flowers into a teapot, pour boiling water over them and steep for five to ten minutes. We love using glass teapots, as they display the beautiful color of each tea.

To serve, pour the steeped tea through a strainer into a cup, let it cool a bit and sweeten with honey.

Many common teas have relaxing as well as medicinal properties:

Peppermint relieves stress, soothes an upset stomach, aids digestion and treats minor headaches.

Lemon balm fights fatigue, anxiety, depression and headaches. It also relieves tension and spasms in the digestive tract and tones the heart and circulatory system.

Thyme soothes headaches, colds, coughs and sore throats.

Sage fights colds, flus and coughs, soothes sore throats, aids digestion, lowers blood sugar in diabetics and relieves menstrual cramping.

Calendula improves overall health by preventing and healing infections and inflammation. It repairs skin damage, detoxifies the body and protects the liver and gallbladder.

Black currant leaves treat rheumatism, sore throats, mouth ulcers and respiratory conditions. They support heart health, relieve stress and serve as a diuretic and anti-inflammatory.

Raspberry leaves treat stomach discomfort, diarrhea and colds. They are a female tonic, alleviating menstrual cramps and facilitating childbirth by toning the uterus. They enrich and encourage the flow of mother's milk.

Strawberry leaves are used as a diuretic and an astringent. They can be used as a tonic to treat diarrhea and intestinal and urinary discomfort. They purify the blood, stimulate digestion and counteract anemia.

Cowslip is used as a diuretic, an expectorant and an antispasmodic. It has a calming effect and is supportive of the respiratory system.

St. John's wort is a tonic for the entire nervous system. It is useful as an antidepressant.

Linden flowers promote perspiration and soothe nerves. They are useful for colds, fevers and tension headaches.

LEMON BALM

CALENDULA

COWSLIP

ST. JOHN'S WORT

LINDEN FLOWERS

WILD THYME

Teas from the Tea Plant

All caffeine-containing teas come from the same plant family – an attractive perennial shrub called *Camellia sinensis*. There are more than two thousand different tea plants divided into two major groups: the Chinese tea plant with leathery, elliptical leaves and the Assam tea plant with soft, pointy leaves.

It is the particular timing of the harvest and the manner of processing that turn the tea leaves into a black, green or white tea. Percentages of caffeine vary in teas and are often listed in comparison to a cup of coffee, with coffee considered as 100 percent.

Some general rules for making tea: always use fresh water – preferably filtered water or spring water. Once tea has steeped for the suggested time period, use a strainer to pour off the tea water completely, either right into cups or into a different container. If tea is not consumed immediately, always remove the leaves to prevent the brew from turning bitter. It is a good idea to have a removable tea leaf insert in your teapot or to use two teapots, one to brew and one to serve. I personally like using two teapots, so that the leaves can have unrestricted space to expand and infuse the water with their flavor. Some inserts do not allow for generous space. Prefer loose tea to tea bags – the tea in tea bags often consists of broken or crushed tea leaves of inferior quality that have lost much of their aroma before you get to use them.

I love to smell the loose tea leaves and to touch them with my fingers before placing them into the tea pot, so I never use a spoon to measure out amounts of tea – I do it by feel.

Black tea is the most processed form of tea from the tea plant. Before the leaves are dried, they are rolled to release enzymes that cause them to oxidize and turn brown. Black tea has a strong taste and contains 80 percent of the caffeine in coffee – the highest amount in teas. To brew black tea, pour boiling water over the leaves and steep for four to five minutes. Well-known black teas are called Assam, Darjeeling and Ceylon.

Oolong lies somewhere between black and green teas in terms of processing – it has less caffeine – 60 percent – and more antioxidants than does black tea. It also has a milder flavor – earthy with a sweet aftertaste. To brew oolong tea, boil water, turn off the heat, and let the water cool for about one minute. Then, pour the water over the tea leaves and steep for two to three minutes. Well-known oolongs are called Formosa and China.

Green tea is among the least processed of the teas. The leaves are steamed and then dried. They retain much of their color and antioxidant content, and their caffeine content is 40 percent. To brew green tea, boil water, turn off the heat, and let the water cool for about one minute. Then, pour the water over the tea leaves and steep for one to three minutes. My favorite Japanese green teas are called *sencha* (straightforward and delicate), *genmaicha* (51 percent tea, 49 percent roasted brown rice – half the caffeine of other green teas with a delightful aroma), and *hojicha* (green tea with a mild roasted flavor).

White tea has only recently made its way to the West. It is the finest of teas with a very delicate flavor and color. It is also the most expensive. White tea is made from immature tea leaves that are picked even before the buds have fully opened. They are covered with fine whitish fuzz, which gives the tea its name. White tea is minimally processed, and it has the highest antioxidant level and the lowest caffeine level – 30 percent – which makes it the most beneficial tea for your health. To brew white tea, boil water, turn off the heat, and let the water cool for about one minute. Pour the water over the tea leaves and steep for five to eight minutes. Look for white teas called white peony or silver needles. I like to add a rose bud to my white tea for a special nuance in aroma.

Nothing is wasted in the harvesting of teas. ***Kukicha***, or **twig tea**, is from the prunings of the tea plant. At different times of the year, clippings are steamed, sun-dried and stored in paper bags for two to three years. The process of aging helps to develop the flavor. As a last step, the twigs are ceremoniously roasted to produce their distinctive aroma. Kukicha is lowest in caffeine: 10 percent. To prepare kukicha, I like to boil then simmer the twigs for three minutes.

DARJEELING

OOLONG CHINA

SENCHA

GENMAICHA

SILVER NEEDLES

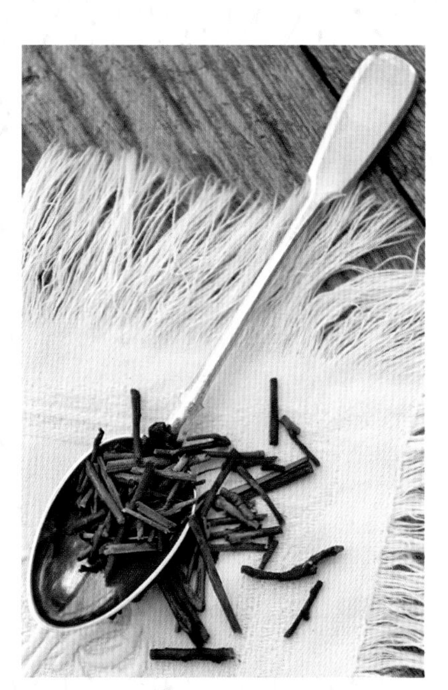

KUKICHA

Yogi Tea

serves 2

This recipe was first given to me by Sat Jivan Kaur, the director of Kundalini Yoga East in New York City, the yoga center where I did my teacher training. It is Yogi Bhajan's ayurvedic alternative to coffee – a delicious and healthful drink that is naturally energizing because it is mineral-rich. It is a great pick-me-up in the afternoon, when many of us experience a drop in energy. The ingredients work together beautifully in synergy and have the following properties:

black pepper	purifies the blood
cardamom	relaxes, benefits colon health
cinnamon	strengthens bones
clove	strengthens the nervous system
ginger	warms, energizes, cleanses, strengthens the nervous system, helps prevent menstrual cramps
black tea	helps with calcium assimilation
milk	helps assimilate minerals from the various spices and prevents stomach and intestinal irritation

2 cups (480 ml) water
4 whole black peppercorns
4 whole pods cardamom, crushed
½ stick cinnamon bark
3 whole cloves
1 slice fresh ginger root
¼ teaspoon black tea
1 cup (240 ml) cold milk
honey

1. Boil the spices in the water in a covered pot for at least 20 minutes. Boil for up to 40 minutes for a stronger brew.
2. Remove from the heat and add the black tea. Steep for 1 to 2 minutes.
3. Strain out the spices and tea leaves.
4. Add the milk and reheat until hot but not boiling.
5. Add honey to taste.

Note: Because it takes a while to make this tea, you can prepare a large batch. Double or triple the recipe and refrigerate the tea before adding the milk and honey. Whenever you would like a cup of yogi tea, take some of the brew, add milk, heat and add honey to taste.

Hot Chocolate

serves 2

There is nothing as satisfying and replenishing as a cup of hot chocolate on a cold afternoon. Cacao is one of the most nutrient-rich foods on this planet. I add a pinch of cayenne pepper for its warmth and for its dilating effect on the capillaries, allowing cacao's nutrients to reach the cells more easily.

- 2 cups (480 ml) milk
- 1 to 2 tablespoons cacao (or unsweetened cocoa) powder
- 1 to 2 tablespoons maple syrup
- 1 teaspoon vanilla extract
- 1 pinch ground cinnamon
- 1 pinch cayenne pepper
- 1 teaspoon coconut oil (optional – for extra richness)

1. Combine the milk and cacao in a pot and heat, stirring continuously, until the cacao dissolves.
2. Add the maple syrup, vanilla, cinnamon, cayenne pepper and coconut oil and bring to a boil.
3. Immediately remove from the heat and pour into cups.

Serve as is or with whipped cream.

Note: When buying cacao powder, get 100 percent cacao, unsweetened. Always look for cacao that has not been treated with alkali. Alkalized cacao may also be called Dutch processed. Prefer organic and fair-trade products. Read more about cacao in the chapter on superfoods (page 284).

Coffee, Alcohol and Carbonated Beverages

Coffee can be beneficial in moderate quantities and when consumed with pleasure. Some of the health benefits include reduced risk of Alzheimer's disease, dementia and Parkinson's disease. Caffeine, the active ingredient in coffee, is a powerful stimulant for both the digestive tract and the nervous system.

Too often, people use coffee to wire up the nervous system when they feel low in energy or need to overcome tiredness. If that use has developed into a daily routine, it might be doing more harm than good. Coffee has a low nutritional profile and does not provide your body with real energy. It wakes you up, but does not replenish the hours of sleep and rest you are missing. In essence, it allows you to push your body to perform beyond its natural capacity.

When you are tired, you need to rest. When you have low energy, you need to nurture your body and eat nutritious food. Consuming too much coffee can lead to an increase in adrenaline production, overtaxed adrenals and heart problems. It can lead to reduced sexual vitality, mineral deficiencies and gastrointestinal problems.

Decaffeinated coffee is gentler on the body, but choose one that has had its caffeine removed by steam and not by toxic solvents.

Many people love the aroma of coffee. If you are one of them, keep a little jar of ground coffee handy and simply sniff it once in a while.

Like caffeine, **alcohol** has extreme yin energy. People often use it to relieve stress and tension, to relax and to create a carefree mindset. The effect, of course, is only temporary. Everybody has a different tolerance level for alcohol. The key – as always – is to find what's right for you. Enjoying a glass of quality wine in good company with your meal can be a pleasant, even health-promoting experience, especially in the case of red wine. Red wine provides the body with a good dose of powerful antioxidants called polyphenols, which help to fight off cancer and reduce the risk of heart attacks and strokes. But frequent consumption of alcohol in large quantities will counteract its benefits. Excessive drinking can damage liver and brain cells and lead to high blood pressure and heart disease.

Carbonated drinks have several characteristics that make them detrimental to your health, and I wholeheartedly recommend avoiding them completely. Sodas contain all kinds of artificial chemicals and dyes. They are also loaded with sugar, corn syrup or artificial sweeteners. Both the carbonation and the phosphoric acid content lead to loss of calcium from your bones. And because carbonated drinks cause you to burp, they allow stomach acid to rise into the esophagus, damaging cells and setting the stage for esophageal cancer. Even carbonated water is not recommended in high quantities. It does not contain sugar or chemicals, but it still causes calcium loss and makes you prone to esophageal cancer for the same reasons that sodas do.

Berries

Berries are the most delicious antioxidant-packed and cleansing food on this planet. Their strong colors allude to these properties. (If you remember from the chapter on vegetables, most antioxidants are pigments.) Berries are low in sugars and high in vitamins, minerals and protective phytochemicals. Did you know that a pound of strawberries has less sugar than one lemon?

Berries, especially their seeds, are fiber rich. They boost the immune system and help to prevent cancer, premature aging and dementia. Eat them by the handful or add them to smoothies, muesli, porridge, salads and desserts.

If you are fortunate enough to have berries growing in your yard, you can eat them fresh off the bush as each variety comes into season. In Estonia you can find many kinds of wild berries, starting with wild strawberries in the early part of summer. The taste of wild strawberries crystallizes the essence of Estonian summers. They are best when eaten as you pick them, still warm from the rays of the sun. I feel so blessed that since we cleared a wooded area behind the house, more and more wild strawberries each year have made our park their home – our park has literally turned into a wild strawberry field. Raspberries and blueberries ripen in July, blackberries and lingonberries in August. You can see people with buckets and baskets combing the forests for these tiny luscious treasures. Cloudberries, which look like orange raspberries but grow one berry per stem, live in the bogs, as do cranberries. There is no more colorful place than a bog in autumn. The cranberries look like little red pearls strewn about a carpet of moss. You can pick them and preserve them simply by keeping them in cold water.

In my garden I grow red, white and black currants as well as red, golden and green gooseberries. Sea-buckthorn has recently become a popular crop in Estonia. It is a very potent berry featuring a vitamin C content 12 times greater than that of an orange. Goji berries have become the rage in the United States. Considered the most nutritious berry, one that even contains complete protein, it is known to help people enjoy longer and healthier lives. Its nickname is "longevity fruit." Eat them as is or brew them into a tea – but be sure to consume both the drink and berries in your goji tea.

Recipes that feature berries are on pages 71, 212, 254 and 264.

Cacao

Some good news: Cacao, also called cocoa – the ingredient that gives chocolate its character – is good for you. Cacao is one of the most nutrient-dense magical foods in the world. It even has a mythological dimension, called the food of gods as well as the food of lovers. Chocolate has the power to uplift our moods, elevate our spirits and open our hearts.

Commercially produced chocolate is, of course, a rather processed food. The purist would say that chocolate needs to be eaten in its raw state, as cacao beans or cacao nibs (the bean crushed into smaller pieces). I remember very vividly my first experience eating raw cacao nibs. I took a teaspoonful into my mouth and slowly began to chew on the crunchy pieces. At first I felt a bit disappointed that the taste wasn't sweet at all. But then my mind shifted toward accepting this new food for whatever it had in store. As the taste grew more intense with prolonged and conscious chewing, I came to recognize the essence of chocolate – it was like a homecoming, like uncovering a gem. I was experiencing the true spirit of chocolate! It was subtle yet powerful. There was a richness and also a purity. I had a sense of upward expansion beyond my body – I felt uplifted, energized and completely present. It was really amazing!

Cacao is a bean that grows in the tropics and contains a host of beneficial components, including magnesium, antioxidants, phenylethylamine, anandamine and tryptophan. Cacao has the highest magnesium content of any food. Magnesium provides support for the heart, increases brainpower, acts as a natural laxative, soothes premenstrual symptoms, relaxes muscles and helps to build strong bones. Antioxidants make up 10 percent of the cacao bean – an exceptionally high percentage. Phenylethylamine, also called the "love chemical," anandamine, also called the "bliss chemical," and tryptophan, the amino acid needed to produce serotonin, the "feel-good chemical," are all mood-enhancing nutrients that produce feelings of euphoria and well-being.

As you can see, cacao has health benefits on the physical as well as the mental plane. It is also considered to be an aphrodisiac. On the spiritual level, cacao has the subtle power to heal and to open our hearts, bringing forth a sense of receptivity, kindness, compassion and love.

Consider the richness of cacao's gifts when you savor your next piece of chocolate. Please slow down and consciously enjoy its many levels. Try a high-quality dark chocolate. The more cacao in the chocolate, the less sugar and additives it can contain. However, as always, read the fine print. It is legal to call 41 percent cacao content a dark chocolate, but chocolate containing at least 70 percent cacao is best.

And if you are really brave, try raw cacao beans or nibs. They are sold at health food stores and through raw food websites such as www.sunfood.com.

Find a recipe for Hot Chocolate on page 278 and for Potent Round Brownies on page 258.

Seaweeds

KELP

ARAME

Seaweeds are the most mineral-rich foods on earth. Their most significant minerals are calcium, iron, phosphorous, sodium and iodine. Eating too many processed foods or foods grown in mineral-depleted soil can result in a lack of minerals in the body, leading to cravings for salty foods. Adding sea vegetables into your food repertoire will replenish mineral levels and alleviate cravings. These vegetables also contain iodine, which balances thyroid activity. Vitamins A, B, C, and E are present in high levels, and surprisingly, the protein content is high as well – up to 38 percent.

Health benefits attributed to seaweeds are numerous. They have the power to detoxify the body from heavy metals and radioactive elements and to counterbalance the effects of X-rays. They strengthen bones and teeth and benefit the nervous and digestive systems. They are helpful in treating tumors and in maintaining healthy skin and hair. They also have antibiotic properties.

Seaweeds are traditionally dried and are sold in their dry form.

People who tend to feel cold easily and who often have cold hands or cold feet should limit themselves to small quantities of seaweeds, which are extremely cooling and might therefore not suit their body types. The body uses its resources to compensate for the cooling effect. This compensation can easily waste energy, deplete reserves and weaken the entire organism.

There are several varieties of seaweeds:

Kelp is a giant in the plant world. Each stalk can grow to be 180 feet long. The kelp family of seaweeds also includes arame, kombu and wakame. In addition to vitamins A, B, C, D and K, kelp contains the trace minerals copper, zinc and chromium. Kelp becomes sweet through cooking. Rehydrate dried kelp and cook it for fifteen minutes.

Arame is a brown kelp with wide leaves that can grow to be a foot long. It has a mild, sweet taste and is delicious sautéed, alone or combined with land vegetables such as carrots and onions, and sprinkled with lemon juice. Arame is useful in the treatment of high blood pressure and female hormonal imbalances.

KOMBU

DULSE

WAKAME

Kombu comes in stalks and can be added to soups and bean, grain or pasta dishes to boost nutrient value. If you add a stalk to these foods while they cook, you can intensify their immune-strengthening and cancer-fighting abilities. Kombu also enhances the flavor of any meal and helps tenderize beans. Try it baked in the oven for a delicious snack.

Wakame is superrich in calcium and acts as a tenderizer, increasing the digestibility of beans and grains as well as fats. It is used most often in soups, especially miso soup. It can also be used as a green in salads. Rehydrate wakame and cook it for ten minutes.

Dulse is red in color and grows in smooth, hand-shaped fronds. It is very high in iron and can be used to strengthen the blood, kidneys and adrenals. It is chewy, has a slightly tangy flavor and is great in salads and stir-fries. Dulse also comes in the form of flakes – sprinkle them over vegetables and soups.

NORI

Nori is washed and chopped into small pieces, then spread over bamboo mats to dry in sheets. The sheets are delicate and crispy, and the color can be dark green to black. The darker the nori, the higher the quality. Nori sheets can be roasted and are used to wrap sushi and rice balls. Nori is very high in vitamin A and is richer in protein than meat.

If you are new to seaweeds, acquaint yourself with this potent food by using one of the "sprinkleable" kinds of seaweed available in health food stores. One such condiment is gomasio, a tasty combination of roasted sesame seeds, sea salt and seaweed. You can also buy sheets of nori and cut them with scissors into little pieces. Sprinkle seaweeds over your vegetables or grains for a mineral boost. Add a piece of kombu or wakame when cooking beans – it will tenderize your beans and enhance both flavor and nutritional value.

Polli Talu Arts Center

Concepts

Polli talu – Estonian for Polli's farm – is a traditional farm complex in the village of Rame, in western Estonia not far from the gentle Baltic Sea. Its structures are built of logs and topped with thatched roofs. When I purchased the farm in 1995, all the roofs were leaking and in need of replacement. I have since restored the farm and transformed it into a multiuse art and wellness center.

At Polli Talu, we host collaborating arts groups of up to 15 people or 30 workshop participants. Our season runs from June through September, with three studios available for booking.

The 27-by-40-foot (8 x 12-m) dance studio has a sprung wooden floor, ideal for dance, yoga and body work. This studio also serves as our performance and exhibition space.

The art studio has a 20-by-30-foot (6 x 9-m) open workspace with a sleeping loft, a kitchen and bathroom facilities.

The writer's studio in the sauna building has a 14-by-20-foot (4 x 6-m) workspace with a fireplace, sleeping loft and kitchenette. The same building contains a traditional wood-burning sauna, complete with showers and a dressing room.

We take good care of our artists and guests by providing three wholesome meals per day made from fresh, whole foods. Produce comes from our own garden, from neighboring farms and from the farmers' market in Pärnu.

Polli Talu Arts Center is truly a gift of time and space. It provides an opportunity for guest artists to focus wholly on creative work without any distractions – no telephones to answer, no errands to run, no need to go food shopping or to spend time in the kitchen preparing meals.

It is also an ideal place to hold workshops, seminars and retreats. Each summer we offer kundalini yoga weekend intensives, tai chi workshops, dance seminars, drumming workshops, whole-foods cooking classes, weeklong yoga and wellness retreats, lectures, performances and exhibitions. The center has been a venue for the international

symposium Dance Across Borders and for international workshops in choreography, music, lighting design, performance and video. We have hosted many international artistic collaborations.

We hold kundalini yoga classes every weekday morning. These classes are open to our guest artists and to our local community – neighbors who participate can pay what they wish or contribute vegetables or flowers from their gardens.

Polli Talu is a phenomenon that is difficult to express in words. It must be experienced. The best metaphor I can come up with is a wooded meadow – a collaboration between people and nature. I was first introduced to wooded meadows in the Läänema district of Estonia. As the name suggests, wooded meadows are areas where singular trees and bushes grow within a meadow. They need continuous care to prevent undergrowth from taking over. Picture an almost parklike environment, a green meadow with gorgeous trees and bushes growing here and there. The creation of this particular environment allows an abundance of different plant species to grow democratically next to each other, without one dominating over another. There is light as well as shadow, and there are perfect amounts of moisture, wind and nutrients. These wooded meadows are very appealing visually, emanating a quiet harmony that instills a sense of inner peace in the observer.

Similarly, Polli Talu is a collaboration between people and nature, a sacred space that provides openness and structure, sunlight and shelter, freedom and concentration, flow and stability. Here, one can rest and work, recharge and relax, go within and meet great people, catch up on sleep and delve into creative work. Life and art melt into one in a beautiful natural rhythm. The pleasant aura of the place and its closeness to nature create a sense of spontaneous well-being. Here you can feel grounded, let go of tension, and become yourself again.

Polli Talu is a place where seeds begin to sprout. Artists are inspired by the stark beauty of the northern landscape and skyscape. Many idea seedlings that took root here have grown and flourished.

Even the traditional art form of building thatched roofs reemerged at Polli Talu. Roof master Elmar Vesker from Virtsu taught two young men in the village how to thatch a roof. The three of them worked together on the farm's main house roof in 1996. By the following summer, the two apprentices were already able to build the storehouse roof by themselves. Since then, they have rethatched many roofs at neighboring farms. Roofs as far away as Sweden and England are the work of these young men from our village.

And seeds of kundalini yoga have been sown throughout Estonia. Many of my yoga students are now instructors in their own right, and interest in kundalini yoga is growing exponentially.

Origins

It all started with a dream – the dream of living in the countryside. I have always had a strong attraction to traditional rural architecture. As a child, I loved to hang out at open-air museums that featured old farm buildings. I love the interconnectedness of their design and the way they function with the nature, climate and culture that surround them. In such places, you get to experience the elements air, fire, water and earth up close.

I thought, what can a dancer, choreographer, yoga instructor and holistic health coach possibly do in the countryside? The answer was obvious: Integrate all that I have learned in life. By integrating my love for the arts, my love for holistic living and my love for cooking, I gave Polli Talu Arts Center its particular feel and created an oasis where the whole person – body, mind and soul – is nourished, inspired, challenged and supported.

At this point in my life, I divide my time between the United States of America and Estonia. I spend summers at the farm and winters in a small town called Beacon in the beautiful Hudson Valley. Every time I come back to the farm, I ask myself, what is it about this place that makes it feel so good? And I realize it is the quality of life it inspires. Its scale makes me feel more human. It is about looking out the window and seeing green fields and meadows and tall trees, opening the door every morning and stepping into the garden to smell the fresh country air, walking over to the dance studio and doing my yoga practice in a gorgeous sunlit space, preparing meals with freshly picked herbs, greens and vegetables, observing my cats as they stretch or relax in the most delicious poses, marveling at the amazing cloud formations the sky keeps producing, enjoying the golden evening light as it shines through our kitchen window, going about my daily work in a more mindful and peaceful manner – keeping life simple and discovering great pleasures and beauty in simplicity.

Holistic Health Coaching

Holistic health coaching is so much more than a profession. It is a way of life. It is a way of making my life a work of art. I practice what I teach and reap the benefits. Over the years, I have seen great changes in my own health and life, from overcoming constipation, increasing energy, strengthening bones and moving gracefully through menopause to daring to dream big.

When in the States, I work one-on-one with my clients. As a holistic health coach I strive to support the whole person, body, mind and spirit. I show women in midlife and early retirement how to consciously make the next 20, 30, even 50 years of their life a work of art.

In my experience, to make any good art takes energy, enthusiasm and desire. The same is true for making your life a work of art. Using the power of effective nutrition, quality of life strategies, building community and reconnecting to their purpose, the women I work with begin to live life on their own terms. Once these pieces of the puzzle have been assembled, making life a work of art comes naturally.

I assist my clients in their quest to cultivate awareness and reclaim their body's wisdom. I gently guide and inspire my clients to make small shifts in their daily habits relating to food, physical activity, relationships and lifestyle. I remind my clients that they are spiritual beings who need to feed their souls as well as their bodies. Gradually and without strain, they integrate healthy habits into their lives and let go of unhealthy habits – those that no longer serve them. This process is truly delightful. There is no need for discipline and deprivation. We focus on the positive and very tangible results of our work together, such as sustained energy throughout the day, improved digestion, enhanced health, greater clarity of mind, a more youthful appearance and a genuine sense of well-being. It is very empowering to experience how much you can do to enhance overall wellness by taking simple steps, changing a few habits, reclaiming responsibility for your own health and life, becoming proactive and assuming the role of conscious cocreator of your own destiny.

In Estonia, I work mostly in group settings. My week-long Passion, Purpose and Pleasure Wellness Retreat is a perfect example. It is so thrilling to watch the transformation that can happen in just one week of relaxation, movement, awareness and eating balanced whole foods. Participants get a chance to immerse themselves instantly in a healthy way of living. We start the morning by drinking a glass of water. Next comes kundalini yoga morning practice, which combines postures, stretching, movement, meditation, breathing and chanting. It stimulates the glands, strengthens the nervous system, opens meridians and balances chakras. Then, we have a wholesome breakfast followed by free time. A pre-lunch hands-on cooking class provides a fun learning experience on how to make simple and delicious meals using fresh and natural foods. Each day we prepare a different three-course meal together – including dessert! Later in the afternoon, I give an interactive talk covering timely nutrition topics such as the energetics of food, the yin and yang of food, complex carbohydrates versus simple sugars, natural versus processed foods, good oils and fats, conscious eating and many others. Breath Walks provide a safe and easy workout that keeps body and heart fit while increasing oxygen levels in the blood. During free time, participants enjoy the therapeutic and relaxing effects of deep tissue massage or gentle Reiki energy work. A wholesome dinner rounds out the culinary aspect of the day. Just before retiring, we practice a meditation to center ourselves and calm our minds in preparation for restful and deep sleep.

Participants have described their feelings before and after the retreat. Before: worn out, bored with daily routines, rushed, tense, hungry, emotionally overtaxed. After: relaxed, joyful, harmonious, balanced, well-rested, nourished on all levels, at peace, spiritually connected, great, confident, light in the body, whole, inspired, full of vitality. It is like turning the clock backward – you bring out the youthful you again.

Each summer, several young people become interns for a month at Polli Talu Arts Center. The internship is a great way for them to learn how to grow, care for, prepare and cook healthful foods. While working and living at Polli Talu, they, too, reap the benefits of living a holistic lifestyle. Many of them are surprised that they have grown fond of eating vegetables. They come to realize how eating less sugar actually leads to more energy. They stop drinking coffee because they no longer feel the need for this source of fake energy.

My favorite story is that of Jaanika. Some time after working at Polli Talu, she got together with her girlfriends in the city. They all went to the supermarket to buy some goodies. While her friends went for chocolate and pastries, Jaanika, after consulting with her body, found that she really was in the mood for cauliflower.

To receive my free newsletter featuring food for thought, nourishing information, health tips and tempting seasonal recipes, please subscribe at **www.MarikaB.com**.

Bibliography

Albi, Johnna and Catherine Walthers. *Greens Glorious Greens! More than 140 Ways to Prepare All Those Great-Tasting, Super-Healthy, Beautiful Leafy Greens.* New York: St. Martin's Press, 1996.

Berley, Peter. *The Modern Vegetarian Kitchen.* New York: William Morrow, 2004.

Colbin, Annemarie. *Food and Healing.* New York: Ballantine Books, 1986.

David, Marc. *The Slow Down Diet: Eating for Pleasure, Energy and Weight Loss.* Rochester, VT: Healing Arts Press, 2005.

Douillard, John. *The 3-Season Diet.* New York: Three Rivers Press, 2000.

Erasmus, Udo. *Fats that Heal, Fats that Kill: The Complete Guide to Fats, Oils, Cholesterol and Human Health.* Burnaby, BC, Canada: Alive Books, 1993.

Fallon, Sally. *Nourishing Traditions.* Washington, DC: New Trends Publishing, 2001.

Gagné, Steve. *Energetics of Food: Encounters With Your Most Intimate Relationship.* Santa Fe, NM: Spiral Sciences, 1990.

Gittleman, Ann Louise. *Get the Sugar Out: 501 Simple Ways to Cut the Sugar Out of Any Diet.* New York: Three Rivers Press, 1996.

Gittleman, Ann Louise. *Your Body Knows Best.* New York: Pocket Books, 1997.

Hensperger, Beth. *Muffins.* New York: Free Press, 2003.

Institute for Integrative Nutrition. www.integrative nutrition.com [website].

Lipski, Elizabeth. *Digestive Wellness.* Lincolnwood, IL: Keats Publishing, 2000.

McEachern, Leslie. *The Angelica Home Kitchen: Recipes and Rabble Rousings from an Organic Vegan Restaurant.* New York: Ten Speed Press, 2004.

Moosewood Collective. *Moosewood Restaurant New Classics.* New York: Clarkson Potter, 2001.

Rosenthal, Joshua. *Integrative Nutrition: The Future of Nutrition.* New York: Integrative Nutrition Publishing, 2006.

Rosenthal, Joshua and Tom Monte. *The Energy Balance Diet.* Indianapolis, IN: Alpha Books, 2003.

Stanchich, Lino. *Power Eating Program: You Are How You Eat.* Chico, CA: George Ohsawa Macrobiotic Foundation, 1989.

Turner, Kristina. *The Self-Healing Cookbook: A Macrobiotic Primer for Healing Body, Mind and Moods with Whole, Natural Foods.* Vashon Island, WA: Earthtones Press, 2002.

Weed, Susun S. *New Menopausal Years: The Wise Woman Way.* Woodstock, NY: Ash Tree Publishing, 2002.

Weill, Andrew and Rosie Daley. *The Healthy Kitchen: Recipes for a Better Body, Life, and Spirit.* New York: Alfred A. Knopf, 2003.

Wolfe, David and Shazzie. *Naked Chocolate: Uncovering the Astonishing Truth about the World's Greatest Food.* Berkeley, CA: North Atlantic Books, 2005.

Wood, Rebecca. *The New Whole Foods Encyclopedia.* New York: Penguin Books, 1999.

Wood, Rebecca. *The Splendid Grain.* New York: William Morrow, 1997.

Yoga Journal. www.yogajournal.com [website].

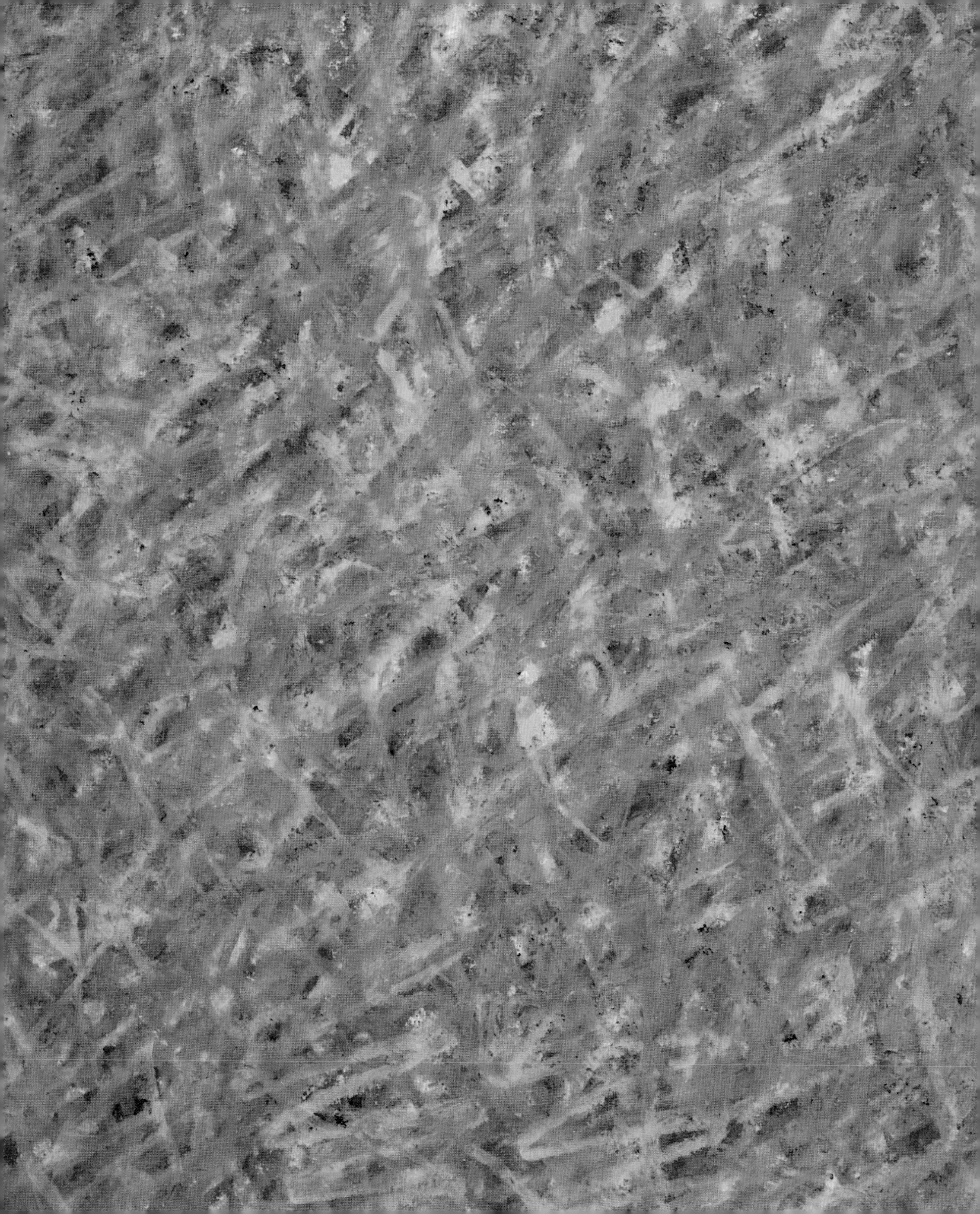

Index

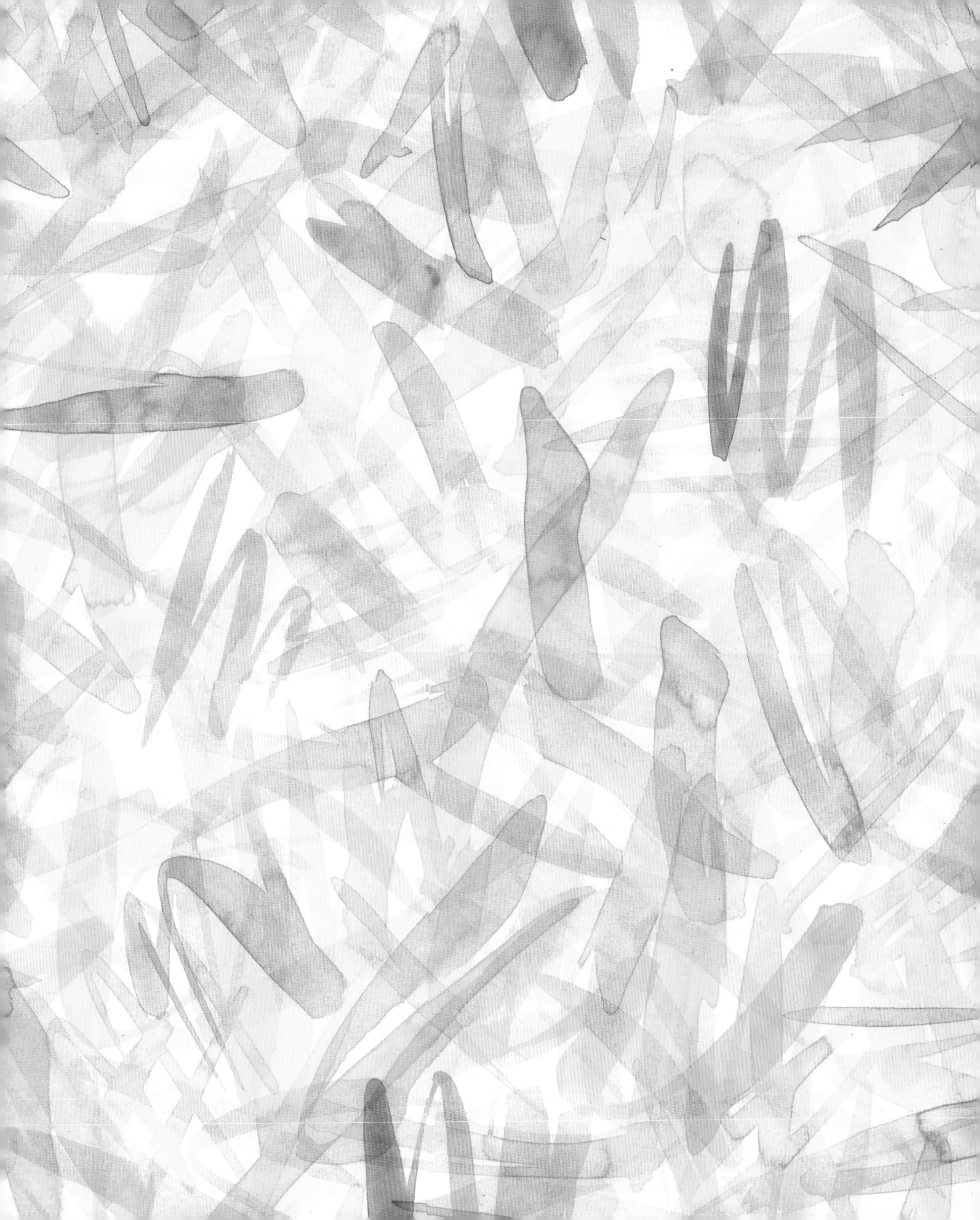